UNLOCKING INDUSTRIAL
RESOURCE PRODUCTIVITY

UNLOCKING INDUSTRIAL RESOURCE PRODUCTIVITY

Five core beliefs to increase profits through
energy, material, and water efficiency

MARKUS HAMMER
KEN SOMERS

McKinsey Publishing
Copyright © 2016 by McKinsey & Company, Inc.
ISBN-13: 978-0-9969949-0-3

CONTENTS

Introduction vii

The resource-productivity imperative 1
Chapter 1   Why resource productivity in operations matters
             more than ever 3
Chapter 2   What resource productivity means for your company 19

Five core beliefs 43
Chapter 3   Think lean 45
Chapter 4   Think limits 63
Chapter 5   Think profit per hour 85
Chapter 6   Think holistic 107
Chapter 7   Think circular 121

The road map for success 147
Chapter 8   Preparing for the corporate-transformation journey 149
Chapter 9   Optimizing your manufacturing site 175
Chapter 10   Your next steps 207

About the authors 220
Web-based resources 222
References 223
Acknowledgements 229

INTRODUCTION

A decade or so ago, companies in industrial manufacturing and other process industries did not need to focus on resource productivity. If they gave any attention to the topic, it was to make small, incremental measures in the hopes of generating marginal improvements. That period is now over. Today, there is no debate: resource productivity must be among the top priorities—if not the top priority—of industrial manufacturers around the world.

Recent shifts in both supply and demand are squeezing these companies from both sides. On the supply side, raw materials are increasingly scarce, making them more difficult and more expensive to procure. At the same time, demographic changes—primarily in emerging markets—are increasing the demand for finished goods. These trends have been building over the past several years, and they will continue to gain momentum. As a result, industrial manufacturers will need to do more with less.

Compounding this problem is the fact that the easy gains have already been captured. Most organizations have already taken the obvious steps—for example, upgrading their lighting and automating their HVAC controls. Yet they are now bumping up against the limits of what they can accomplish using a traditional approach. Why? The fundamental premise of that approach—in which resource productivity is subordinate to other operational priorities—is no longer valid.

For example, many managers still assume that these measures will only serve as a hindrance to plant operations—an opposing force that makes their daily work more difficult. Others assume that they simply don't need these measures. (This is a line we hear frequently when meeting with companies: "Our plant is already as efficient as it can be.") Yet there are always opportunities to transform a process or facility, improving efficiency and yield, and generating clear financial benefits, often with little or no capital expenditure.

To capture these gains, however, organizations need a better approach to resource productivity. They need to embed new ways of thinking—core beliefs—in their management teams, workforces, and organizational cultures. We use the word "belief" deliberately, because it underscores the way that change comes from thinking about productivity in a whole new way.

Specifically, our approach centers on five core beliefs:

1. Think lean: In the original application of lean, companies analyzed the value stream of a particular manufacturing process and ruthlessly cut away anything that did not clearly add value. This methodology is highly synergistic with resource productivity, which applies similar rigor and looks at all steps of a process, seeking to eliminate anything that leads to wasted resources, in both energy and materials.

Lean is an extremely useful way of thinking about resource productivity because it uses well-known principles—like standardization and continuous improvement—that a broad base of managers and leaders already know and likely use. Similarly, it relies on best practices such as performance meetings and integrated KPIs, which are likely to be in place already and translate easily to resource-productivity initiatives. Perhaps most important, it is extremely comprehensive and bottom up. The best ideas often come from line walks with workers who feel empowered to make suggestions and drive improvements, fostering a more inclusive process and leading to better results.

2. Think limits: In the traditional approach to resource productivity, companies typically start with their existing process as a baseline, and then seek to make incremental improvements from there. The second of our core beliefs, think limits, flips this concept on its head. Instead of using the current process as a baseline, it calculates the theoretical limit of that process—meaning the output from an ideal version, with no mechanical or chemical losses and perfect energy utilization—and establishes that as the baseline. Such a goal is clearly unattainable in the real world, but this approach leads to a more comprehensive means of identifying and reducing losses. It creates an ambitious, "stretch" target that companies then seek to achieve. (Often, the calculation alone identifies categories of loss and waste that the facility managers were not previously aware of.)

3. Think profit per hour: The third core belief—thinking in terms of profit per hour—helps align objectives for the organization. This is critical, because different productivity initiatives often have different goals, which can conflict with each other. Production managers, for example, strive for improvements in output, while energy managers focus on reducing energy consumption. Which one takes precedence? More often than not, the managers themselves don't know. Reconciling these issues requires a powerful new metric: profit per hour.

At the highest level, profit per hour calculates an operation's gross profit for any given period of time by subtracting overall costs, including energy and resources, from revenue. It is a real-time, operational metric that helps organizations break down silos, giving managers clear visibility into the relationship between different productivity measures. More important, it generates a quantitative—and thus definitive—answer to the question of which measures should be organizational priorities.

4. Think holistic: Despite the best intentions, many companies fall short of their resource-productivity goals. Why? Success requires a thorough change-management effort. Managers must set meaningful and achievable goals, and persuade often reluctant organizations to embrace and pursue them. They must secure the buy-in of their employees, and equip them with the skills and deploy the new management systems needed to improve the way the organization functions.

Colleagues of ours at McKinsey spent three years surveying some 600,000 managers, 7,000 senior executives, and leading academics to explore why some transformations fail and others succeed. The results showed that successful transformations are based on three core elements that drive each other like interlocking gears. First are technical systems, meaning the assets and equipment a company owns and the processes people perform with those assets to create value. Second is management infrastructure—the formal structures, processes, and systems that companies use to manage people and the technical systems. Third are mindsets and behaviors, or the attitudes that drive behavior individually and collectively. Successful companies apply a holistic approach that encompasses all three, making them better able to implement and sustain changes to improve resource productivity.

5. Think circular: At a basic level, the global economy relies on taking raw materials out of the ground and making them into finished products, which ultimately get thrown away. It's a very linear logic—"take, make, dispose"—yet it's not sustainable in the long run. Instead, the fifth and final core belief is that organizations need to move beyond this linear approach and "think circular." That is, they should treat supply chains as circles, where they can create new value by looping products, components, and materials back into the production process after they have fulfilled their utility over the product life cycle. This is a complex endeavor—it requires designing products in a new way, adopting business models that go beyond a mere one-time sale, and revamping supplier relationships.

Underlying tools

To help companies transform these five core beliefs into practices that reduce resource consumption, decrease the unit price of resources, and optimize product mix and pricing, we and our colleagues have developed a wide range of analytical models, metrics, and other concepts that companies can apply to Some tools apply directly to specific core beliefs, however, they are intended as a set of potential options, not prescriptions. No two companies—or even two facilities in the same company—have an identical set of resource-productivity issues. Accordingly, company leaders should pick and choose those tools that best fit their needs. The core beliefs are universally applicable, but the tools are discretionary.

In conclusion, we have been studying resource productivity for almost a decade and helping companies transform their operations for greater efficiency in both energy use and yield. Collectively, the ideas discussed in this book have already generated hundreds of millions of euros in savings. (We have also interspersed our argument with actual examples of how companies have implemented these measures.)

This publication summarizes our experience and McKinsey's thinking on resource productivity. It is intended to be a handbook for leaders of industrial manufacturers and other process industries. We're excited to put our ideas down on paper as a resource to other organizations. In addition, we believe that the business imperative is clear. Company leaders—from the executive team down to the managers and shift supervisors of individual plants—have the power to give their companies a true competitive edge. Increasingly, winning companies will seize this opportunity, starting today.

Part 1

THE RESOURCE-PRODUCTIVITY IMPERATIVE

Resource productivity is a complex challenge, and it's growing more difficult over time. Yet the approach that many companies use—a series of small measures at the margins of their operations—is increasingly falling short. As raw materials become more scarce and expensive, resource productivity will begin to separate winning companies from the rest. Yet before company leaders can transform their operations, they need to understand the scope of the current situation.

CHAPTER 1

WHY RESOURCE PRODUCTIVITY IN OPERATIONS MATTERS MORE THAN EVER

A confluence of forces is intensifying the demand for resources, even as other forces are making it more difficult and expensive to find and use new sources of supply. The clash of these two sets of forces is creating a world where resource prices are already soaring and are expected to stay high, where owners of the most sought-after resources make the biggest profits, and where commodity companies that must buy from the owners are seeing their margins shrink. But while this scenario presents challenges, it also opens up new opportunities for manufacturers that are able to learn how to extract greater productivity from resources used in their operations.

Forces driving up the demand for resources

In the very short run, commodity prices and supply/demand balances are heavily influenced by economic conditions in major consuming countries and industries. China's growth slowdown has dampered prices recently, for example. Over the longer haul, though, a number of forces are coming together in ways that will put the world's resources— energy, materials, land, food, water—under mounting pressure in the coming decades. Of these, the exploding global population is only the most obvious. Since 1994, the global population (the number of living humans on the planet) has grown from 5.7 billion to 7.2 billion. Despite slowing population growth, UN projections suggest that the world's population could reach 9.6 billion by 2050, with most of the increase concentrated in the poorest countries.[1]

Rising wealth per capita will further intensify pressure on resources by adding 3 billion new middle-class consumers to the world's economy to the 1.8 billion such consumers already out there by 2030. In many countries, as incomes rise, so does the demand for resources—steel for automobiles, land to raise livestock for meat consumption, materials for the construction of homes. Indeed, we expect the number of cars globally to double to 1.7 billion by 2030.[2]

And as city populations continue to expand, the demand for resources overall as well as urban infrastructure—residential and commercial space, medical facilities, public transportation networks—will soar further. In China and India, for example, where more new cities are forming than anywhere else in the world, the McKinsey Global Institute projects that 750 million more people will be living in cities in 2030 than today. In addition, up to three billion people in Asia could join the middle class. Over the next two decades, boosting demand and putting the resource system under great stress.[3]

The demand for most resources has grown strongly since 2000, and this is a trend that will likely continue over the next several decades. To illustrate, by 2030, the demand for primary energy is expected to rise by

---

1   "Challenges Facing World Population Take Centre Stage at Annual UN Forum," *un.org,* last modified April 7, 2014, http://www.un.org/apps/news/story.asp?NewsID= 47520&Cr=population &Cr1=#.U3Jzw_ldV8E.

2   Dobbs, Richard, Jeremy Oppenheim, and Fraser Thompson: "A new era for commodities: Cheap resources underpinned economic growth for much of the 20th century. The 21st will be different," *mckinsey.com,* last modified November 2011, http://www.mckinsey. com/insights/energy_resources_materials/a_new_era_for_commodities.

3   For more information see the full McKinsey Global institute report by Richard Dobbs, Jeremy Oppenheim, Fraser Thompson, Marcel Brinkman, and Marc Zornes: "Resource revolution: Meeting the world's energy, materials, food, and water needs," *mckinsey.com,* last modified November 2011, http://www.mckinsey.com/insights/ energy_resources_materials/resource_revolution.

33 percent; for steel, 80 percent; for food, 27 percent; and for water, 41 percent.[4]

Moreover, tight linkages among resources mean that higher demand for one type of resource can drive stronger demand for other types (Exhibit 1). The reason is that some resources represent a large proportion of inputs needed for the use of other resources. For example, agriculture accounts for nearly 70 percent of the use of water worldwide and roughly 2 percent of the global energy demand. Mineral resources, such as rare earth metals and iron ore, are critical inputs for energy technologies including solar photovoltaics and offshore oil. Additionally, unconventional oil extraction methods such as horizontal drilling use more than four times as much steel as traditional vertical drilling.

Exhibit 1

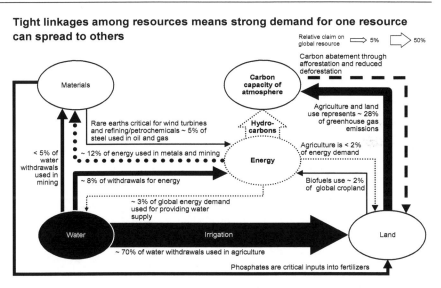

Tight linkages among resources means strong demand for one resource can spread to others

SOURCE: McKinsey Global Institute, "Resource revolution: Meeting the world's energy, materials, food, and water needs," November 2011

---

4   Global insight, IEA, UNEP, FAO, World Steel Association, McKinsey analysis, as cited in the source above, p. 35, exhibit 9.

Forces restricting the supply of resources

Even as the demand for resources escalates to unheard-of levels, other forces will tighten constraints on the availability and quality of supply. Overall, resources have become more difficult and thus costly to extract. Take iron ore. New mining discoveries have been flat despite a fourfold increase in exploration. Iron ore requires large mining systems, and existing systems are operating at close to maximum capacity. Yet new large systems are ruled out for geopolitical and risk reasons. Thus, new systems are smaller as well as more expensive. Meanwhile, the quality of ore is degrading, because typically the longer a mine is in operation, the lower the quality of the mine stock becomes; the best materials are usually extracted first. Land is another example. Though there are still large tracts of uncultivated, unforested, and productive land available around the world, accessing it will prove challenging—much of it is located in politically unstable countries. Likewise, almost half of all new copper projects are in places with a high risk of sociopolitical instability.

Along with the outrun of supply by demand and the higher costs associated with new supply, prices of commodities (steel, pulp, paper, and food) have increased sharply since 2000, erasing all of the price declines seen during the 20th century (Exhibit 2). Of course, technological advances could help decrease the cost and difficulty of finding new supplies of resources and extracting or using them. Likewise, entirely new circumstances, such as the discovery of large shale gas reserves in the United States, could help amellorate the problem. The rise of shale gas has reduced gas prices drastically in the United States. Shale gas exploration in other regions, such as the European Union, has not shown the same abundance and ease of access as in the United States, limiting the global impact on availability of supply.

However, technological advances are difficult to predict. Moreover, relying on the hope that "somebody else" will discover a new technological advancement might be a slippery slope. Additionally, people have short memories, and many forget that the cheap gas in the United States today still costs considerably more to buy than it did in the 1990s. The harsh fact remains that, as we approach shortterm limits on resource supplies,

EXHIBIT 2

Commodity prices have spiked since 2000

Strong resource price increase last decade
McKinsey Commodity Price Index (years 1999 - 2001 = 100)[1]

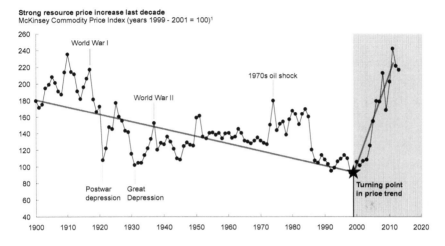

1 Based on arithmetic average of 4 commodity subindices: food, nonfood agricultural items, metals, and energy

SOURCE: Grilli and Yang; Pfaffenzeller; World Bank; International Monetary Fund; Organisation for Economic Co-operation and Development statistics; UN Food and Agriculture Organization; UN Comtrade; Ellen MacArthur Foundation and McKinsey circular economy team

and as we experience even small increases in demand for those resources, volatility in resource prices will only worsen. Indeed, resource-price volatility has already reached an all-time high, second only to the energy price shocks of the 1970s.

Environmental constraints are only worsening the problem. For one thing, the planet's ability to absorb waste streams, including carbon dioxide, is becoming unsustainable. Recent scientific research has found, with 95 percent certainty, that the observed warming over the past half-century is primarily due to human activity.[5] Moreover, climate change is putting the supply of key resources at risk. For instance, water shortages will likely spread owing to changing climatic and precipitation patterns along

---

5 "Climate Change, 2013, The Physical Science Basis," *ipcc.ch,* 2013, http://www.ipcc.ch/report/ar5/wg1.

with pollution and source water contamination, in addition to increasing demand, unsustainable withdrawal rates, and difficulty in finding new supplies. In China alone, water shortages are reducing industrial production by USD 28 billion annually.[6] All this has led to increased pressure on polluters to cut their use of resources and production of waste.

Ramifications for manufacturers

As the demand for resources intensifies, even as those very resources become more constrained and more expensive or volatile in terms of price, building new assets—infrastructure, consumer products, industrial equipment—will also become more expensive. Manufacturers buying essential inputs from resource owners will, therefore, have to raise the prices on their offerings to safeguard their profit margins in the face of increased capital costs.

Moreover, as commodity prices grow ever more volatile, these manufacturers will have less and less control over their costs. Indeed, rising energy and raw material prices mean that variable costs now account for a far larger fraction of overall production costs than they did even a decade ago. In a modern Western steel plant at 2012 pricing, variable costs (energy, materials, and waste) made up 75 percent of the total cost of the steel produced—up from 50 percent in 2000, mainly owing to jumps in commodity prices. In a Chinese plant, lower labor costs meant that the fraction of production costs that were now variable reached as high as 90 percent. And for a company that made LCD televisions, energy represented as much as 45 percent of the total cost of production over the full production chain.

Finally, as consumer groups become more sensitive to the sustainability of products, companies that ignore this sensitivity risk are incurring damage to their brands. In response, some companies are beginning to work in new ways with their suppliers to improve their energy efficiency.

---

6 Mazo, Jeffery: "Asian Environmental Concerns," *Adelphi Series,* October 2008, Volume 48, Number 400, pp. 133 -146.

EXHIBIT 3

Value pools are concentrated upstream

2013 return on invested capital (including goodwill), percentage[1]

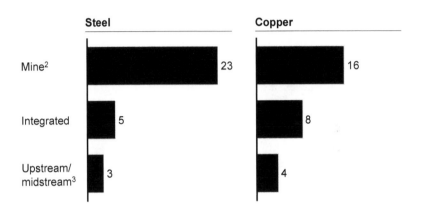

	Steel	Copper
Mine[2]	23	16
Integrated	5	8
Upstream/midstream[3]	3	4

1 Based on a sample of 32 companies: 19 in steel and 13 in copper
2 Mining-related activities, defined as iron ore companies for steel and copper mining companies for copper
3 Smelting and refinery-related activities

All of this spells trouble for commodity manufacturers' bottom lines. Meanwhile, the businesses that own the resources in question (mining companies, oil companies) will increasingly claim the lion's share of available value in such forms as profits and return on invested capital (Exhibit 3).

Something needs to change if manufacturers are to sustain financial health in regard to revenue, profit, share price, and brand strength.

Limits of current efforts

To ensure adequate financial performance in the future, manufacturers have considered or initiated a number of actions such as using new resources, investing in a quest for new supply sources, striving to incrementally improve efficiency in the way they currently use resources, and even redesigning their products. While such approaches offer some promise, they have constraints of their own.

For example, when it comes to using new resources, the payback period for investments in cogeneration plants (which use a heat engine or power station to simultaneously generate electricity and useful heat) can be about five years, which is typically too long for most companies. Another example, wind power, presents the challenge of transporting the energy efficiently from the available land to the urban population centers where it is needed.

Regarding striving for incremental operational improvements in resource efficiencies, additional improvements would satisfy only a fraction of the demand we expect to see by 2030. For instance, improvements in steel production efficiency would meet just 13 percent of that demand. For water, the number is 18 to 21 percent; for primary energy, it's 22 percent. And for land, the figure is 25 to 29 percent.

As for investing in expanding supply sources, McKinsey analysis indicates that supply would have to increase by considerably higher percentages than it did over the past 20 years to satisfy demand in the next few decades, owing to the large expected increases in demand. In the case of primary energy, 32 percent more exajoules will be needed to meet the increase in demand by 2030 than was needed to fulfill demand during the 1990 to 2010 period. For steel, the number is 57 percent more million tons of iron ore. For water, the figure is 139 percent more cubic kilometers. And for land, it's as much as 178 to 250 percent more million hectares of cropland. These numbers are discouraging because companies are already struggling to satisfy the global demand for these commodities and shortages (for example, in clean water) have already begun plaguing many regions.

Manufacturers can also redesign their products to become more resource productive, though this often requires a wider view on what a product constitutes. That is, companies need to move from a product view to a business model view, which may entail thinking of themselves as providers not necessarily of products but of services. Moreover, businesses must not only take into account the cost and value of their offerings but also their total capital requirements and all associated business activities such as maintenance and services.

Interestingly, some current taxation schemes do not promote resource efficiency. This is because most of the taxation burden is placed on labor. (Decoupling, in which a utility's profits are separated from its production of energy, is, of course, a notable exception.[7]) Consider: in Europe, the tax wedge level (the difference between what employees take home in earnings and what it costs to employ them) ranges from 20 percent to about 50 percent of total labor cost for low-wage earners.[8] In general, labor costs (which include taxes) constitute up to 30 percent of production costs in Europe.[9] In EU member states, a high level of labor tax coexists with relatively low levels of other taxes (such as those on environmental impact and consumption).[10] All of this shifts attention to labor instead of resource productivity. The European Union would like to shift taxation away from labor—especially with regard to low-wage and second-income earners—towards taxation that's less detrimental to growth. For example, increasing consumption, environmental, and wealth taxation could help alleviate the tax burden on labor. In one document, the European Commission showed that a shift of taxes away from labor resulted in an increase of 8.9 percent in tax revenue per unit of energy used during the 2008 to 2011 period, compared with a decrease of 0.8 percent on income tax return on labor in the same period.[11]

7   Lazar, Jim, Wayne Shirley, and Frederick Weston: "Revenue Regulation and Decoupling: A Guide to Theory and Application, (The Regulatory Assistance Project)," *raponline.org,* June 2011, http://www.raponline.org/document/download/id/902.

8   Joint European Commission and OECD project, tax and benefits indicators database, *Tax Burden on Labour,* 2013, http://ec.europa.eu/europe2020/pdf/themes/20_tax_burden_on_labour.pdf.

9   European Commission Staff, *Commission staff working document: Energy prices and costs report,* March 17, 2014, http://ec.europa.eu/energy/doc/2030/20140122_swd_prices.pdf.

10 Joint European Commission and OECD project, tax and benefits indicators database, *Tax Burden on Labour,* 2013, http://ec.europa.eu/europe2020/pdf/themes/20_tax_burden_on_labour.pdf.

11 Taxation and Customs Union, *European Commission's Taxation Papers, working papers N.34–2012, Tax Reforms in EU Member States: Tax Policy Challenges for Economic Growth and Fiscal Sustainability, 2012 Report,* 2012, http://ec.europa.eu/taxation_customs/resources/documents/taxation/gen_info/economic_analysis/tax_papers/taxation_paper_34_en.pdf.

The trouble with tradition

The problem with some of the more traditional approaches is that they focus on slivers of operations within the four walls of a manufacturer's business. Moreover, approaches such as lean manufacturing (which in theory aims to eliminate nonvalue-adding activities from all cost areas) don't fully address energy or resources and their constraints because they focus on labor and asset productivity. Also, in the vast majority of use cases, lean tools such as material and information flow analysis do not factor into energy. In short, the absence of a systematic approach that also focuses on resources throughout the value chain causes manufacturers to take a narrow approach.

In addition, in most manufacturing environments, getting more from resources is far from straightforward. Executives and managers assume—sometimes wrongly—that achieving this goal requires heavy investment in new plants and equipment. And, typically, no one person or function in the organization takes end-to-end responsibility for overall margin optimization. Nor does every company have access to the tools, skills, and organizational attributes needed to optimize the use of resources. This often results in a "lever view," whereby companies first identify levers for change and then try to find problems to apply those levers to. Instead, they should start by identifying losses and then finding the specific levers needed to reduce them.

Beyond the organizational issues, companies face tough technical challenges. Manufacturing processes can be complex and comprise many steps, with multiple recycling loops and strong interrelationships between operating parameters (such as raw material qualities, throughput, and process settings including temperatures, pressures, and yield). In addition, most attempts to optimize resource use involve trade-offs; for instance, between throughput and energy consumption, or between a process's yield and the amount of water it consumes for cooling, thereby producing wastewater through the purge process. On top of this, changes in process variables—production speeds, the timing of change-overs between different product types, the aging of key manufacturing equipment—can all affect a process's overall performance in terms of profit per hour.

The traditional approach to these difficult interrelationships has often been to ignore them. Some companies have used lean tools to boost throughput and increase asset and labor productivity, for example. Or, they've made targeted interventions to cut energy consumption or improve yields, assuming that positive changes they make in one area may have deleterious effects in other areas.

To overcome these issues and get the most value from the resources needed in their operations, manufacturers must adopt a decidedly new mind-set. And doing so starts by recognizing that the landscape of opportunity is much broader than they previously assumed. To capture that full opportunity, they need to look beyond their four walls to collaborations with other organizations and stake-holders as well as with customers. In addition, they must focus their attention on resources throughout their industry's value chain, not just those in the links that they directly control.

Perhaps most important, they must not only aim for resource efficiency—which centers on reducing losses—but also for what we call resource productivity: transforming their operations to get greater output (more product, more assets, more sales, more profit) from every resource unit that they use.

The opportunity: Enhancing resource productivity

Resource-productive operations (which cover all resources, with the exception of human, capital, and assets) are about much more than just energy efficiency. Such operations can produce important gains for a company on multiple fronts:

- **Energy:** Minimize energy use and related carbon emissions.
- **Raw materials:** Maximize raw material conversion into finished product (yield) or the most valuable by-products.
- **Emissions:** Minimize direct process emissions, such as CO_2, NO_x, and SO_x.
- **Water:** Reduce loss of water to the ecosystem, avoid losses from factors such as heat or contaminants that the water is carrying, and improve treatment and recovery of materials and energy from wastewater.
- **Waste:** Reduce or avoid waste streams, such as packaging and organic solvents, and increase reuse, recycling, and energy recovery.

Much as is the case with lean, capturing resource productivity can create longterm advantages in costs, risk reduction, and innovation that would be very hard to duplicate. Such gains both maximize the financial benefits accruing to a company and minimize the impact of the industrial process on the environment— which ultimately benefits everyone. What's more, we believe that up to double-digit energy improvements can be achieved across many sectors, including steel manufacturing, chemicals, refining, pulp and paper, consumer goods, automotive and assembly, and logistics. And our experience suggests that the payback period for investments made to achieve energy savings could be a period less than three years. There is even more potential accessible when companies consider resource productivity as a strategic asset requiring positive net present value at classical weighted average cost of capital.

We have seen companies that have taken steps to increase their resource productivity unlock significant financial value, minimizing costs while also establishing greater operational stability. Our experience with clients, as well as our analysis of more than a hundred studies, suggests that manufacturers could reduce the amount of energy they use in production by as much as 10 to 30 percent, depending on the industry and the amount of energy going into the product. For managers who argue that such gains must require extensive capital expenditures, our analysis of one consulting engagement with a large chemical group shows otherwise: although one-third of the company's targeted energy savings required a significant capital investment to achieve the savings, one-third of the target required a relatively small capital investment—and one-third required little to no new capital expenditure. Equally interesting, the average payback period on the investments made by this company was only about one year, and all measures had paybacks within two years.

Through savvy product and packaging design, companies can also reduce material use by 30 percent while at the same time increasing potential for the recycling and reuse of materials and components. Recycling and reuse, in turn, could cut their product costs in half.

Some companies have even begun pioneering new business models that enable them to retain ownership of the materials used in the products they sell. This can involve establishing mechanisms that prompt customers to return a product to its manufacturer at the end of its utility for the consumer—enabling the manufacturer to extract additional value from it. For instance, a UK-based retailer is piloting a take-back program for its power tools. Customers can exchange used tools for cash or a charity donation. The company plans to refurbish the tools it collects in Europe for resale locally or to recycle them and thus recover raw materials that could be used to make new tools at the company's facilities in China. Other companies have made notable strides in packaging and even in components such as the pallets that equipment is shipped on. Our research suggests that the margin improvement potential—resulting primarily from savings in materials costs—could be as high as ten percentage points.

The concept lying at the heart of resource productivity is a simple but powerful one: the use of fewer resources to make more money and increase return to shareholders. By adopting this approach, companies gain an explicit picture of the impact of different product specifications, manufacturing equipment, and process parameters on the overall resource productivity of their operations. Informed by this picture, they can improve their resource productivity in two ways. First, they can identify the most efficient way to organize and control production given the current constraints related to equipment and production scheduling. Second, they can zero in on the biggest opportunities to improve resource productivity— by locating the primary sources of losses in the system. They can thus focus their improvement efforts or capital investments on the areas that will deliver the best possible return.

Technology advances are making it more feasible than ever to adopt the resource-productivity approach. For instance, many companies today have a rich and relatively accessible historical picture of how their manufacturing processes have been performing. Even more important, highly sophisticated tools for analyzing large, complex data sets about manufacturing processes have emerged. Examples include the use of support vector machines and multivariable regression analyses as well as the application of neural network models to spot signals in "noisy" process data. Such tools now offer a fast, effective route to useful insights, pushing the boundaries on resource productivity even further.

A case in point: Reducing energy use and improving yield at Solvay

Coauthored by Alain Michel from Solvay

Founded in 1863, Belgium-based Solvay is one of the world's largest chemical players. In 2013, it recorded EUR 9.9 billion in net sales. 40 percent of its sales are in emerging high-growth countries, and 90 percent of its sales are in markets where it ranks among the top three manufacturers. The company employs 29,400 people in 56 countries.

Solvay is strongly committed to sustainable development and operational excellence. It also has a long history of innovation. Its founder, Ernest Solvay, invented the major industrial process for the production of soda ash, which is used in the manufacturing of glass, paper, and soaps as well as in processes for water treatment and the removal of sulfur dioxide in power stations. Soda ash production is important and widespread today.

Energy is a critical resource for Solvay, playing a major role in its manufacturing operations. The company sources its energy primarily from electricity and natural gas but also from steam and solid fuels. Its total annual energy cost is EUR 1.56 billion. However, the company's culture has historically focused on engineering and workplace safety, rather than on energy efficiency.

In 2010, owing to the strategic importance of energy for the company's production base and a longtime focus on social responsibility, Solvay set an ambitious goal to reduce its global energy consumption by 20 percent, its global greenhouse gas emissions by 20 percent, and its car fleet CO_2 emissions by 30 percent by the year 2020. Its strategy for reaching this goal hinged on improving its main manufacturing processes through the implementation of the best available technologies. In addition, the company established a program called SOLWATT, which focused on strengthening overall energy management in Solvay's production units by deploying new approaches to performance management and behavioral change.

Launched in 2011, SOLWATT has been deployed at 41 manufacturing sites to date, each chosen for their important contribution to overall energy consumption. At each site, teams map the site's energy production and consumption; determine energy losses to identify levers for improving energy efficiency, sourcing, and asset optimization; quantify potential gains and corresponding investments; and define a road map to capture the gains.

One focus of the program has been the use of detailed process analysis to identify losses of energy in sites' production processes. Such losses fall into two categories: incidental (associated with process and equipment and design) and operational (associated with shop-floor management processes). Teams then generate ideas for transforming operations to minimize losses as well as extract more value from resources in the form of increased yield.

Ideas have included rethinking the way that physical assets and resources are configured and optimized. For example, teams identified equipment that was running at higher than optimal temperatures and brainstormed ideas for lowering temperatures through more effective regulation of steam. Additional examples of operational changes included fine-tuning key operational parameters and improving the reliability of manufacturing equipment by modifying key components.

Solvay initially assessed the conventional "big-capital-expenditure" approach and identified a 10 percent improvement opportunity with an average payback of three to five years. The SOLWATT approach is well on its way to finding similar savings—but with an average payback of just one year. To date, using the SOLWATT approach, Solvay has identified and recorded energy-cost savings totaling EUR 73 million.

These kinds of insights can be startling—and can lead to improvements that go straight to a company's bottom line. To illustrate, take the example of a manufacturing plant that had a strong record of efficiency improvements. Its engineers operated equipment at very high levels of availability, and processes were under tight control. The engineers had become accustomed to searching for singledigit percentage increases in yield or energy consumption reductions. But when the company analyzed its process performance data, it was able to identify about a dozen straightforward process changes that helped it reduce the waste of a high-value raw material by as much as 20 percent and to cut overall energy consumption by 15 percent. Together, these two gains enabled the company to decrease its overall costs by 3 to 5 percent—an amount equivalent to its total labor input across the plant.

***

A combination of soaring demand for resources, dwindling supply, and rising energy and raw material prices is eroding profit margins for manufacturers and forcing them to pay as much attention to their variable costs as they do to their fixed costs. To safeguard their financial health in the coming decades, they will need to find new ways of using fewer resources as well as extracting more value— including profit—from the resources they do use.

Trying to expand supply, striving to gain additional incremental efficiencies from manufacturing processes, or relying on traditional tactics such as lean manufacturing won't be enough to solve the problem looming on the horizon. Instead, companies will need to master a new discipline: enhancing resource productivity. Although doing so will require different skills and a decidedly new mind-set, the payoff will be well worth the investment: bottom-line gains derived from doubledigit cost savings paired with yield improvements.

CHAPTER 2

WHAT RESOURCE PRODUCTIVITY MEANS FOR YOUR COMPANY

Manufacturers seeking to enhance resource productivity must adopt new ways of thinking. For example, companies need to shift from the linear, "take, make, and dispose" supply chain metaphor to one of supply circles. They also need to resist the allure of common myths about resource productivity. Such myths make it all too easy to assume that a company has already done everything it can to get more value from the resources it uses. They thus discourage executives from exploring the potential of resource-productivity enhancement. To combat these myths, manufacturers can adopt five core beliefs: think lean, think limits, think profit per hour, think holistic, and think circular.

From supply chains to supply circles

As we saw in Chapter 1, dramatic increases in the demand for resources, combined with restrictions on availability and quality of supply, are driving commodity prices—and price volatility—to new heights. This combination of forces is raising variable costs for companies in resource-intensive industries, such as steel production and chemicals, putting increasing pressure on their profit margins and returns on capital employed (ROCE). All the while, the lion's share of profits is shifting to resource owners. Mines, for example, tend to enjoy after-tax ROCE of 25 to 30 percent, whereas steel production companies' ROCE is closer to 5 percent.

To safeguard their profit margins, companies in resource-intensive industries need to improve their resource productivity—by using fewer resources for each unit of output from their manufacturing operations and by extracting greater value (sales, profitability, product produced) from each unit of resources used. One way to enhance the productivity of resources is to stop thinking and acting like a link in an industry's supply chain—and start thinking and acting like a member of what we call the supply circle.

The supply circle opportunity

Comparing the "chain" and "circle" metaphors produces valuable insights. Upon consideration, the phrase "supply chain" evokes an image in which materials are collected in one place and ultimately disposed of in another. One can envision a massive system of conveyor belts directing materials and energy from places rich in resources to manufacturing powerhouses and then spiriting the resulting products onward to destinations where they are used, discarded, and replaced. In this linear, one-way, "take, make, and dispose" production model—sometimes described as "from cradle to grave"—customers are thought of as consumers. And the model has dominated global manufacturing since the onset of the Industrial Revolution.

By contrast, the phrase "supply circles" emphasizes that value is created—and thus resource productivity is increased—by looping products, components, and materials back into the production process after they have fulfilled their utility over the life cycle of a product (Exhibit 4). Unlike supply chains, supply circles restore materials, energy, and labor inputs—replacing the notion of disposability with restoration and moving away from the "take, make, and dispose" system by designing and optimizing products for multiple cycles of disassembly and reuse. We think of it as "cradle to cradle." This effort starts with materials that are viewed and treated as valuable stock to be used again, not as elements that flow through an industry's value chain just once. And it views customers as users, not consumers.

A supply circle approach to manufacturing operations not only benefits the environment and society but also businesses themselves. Indeed, a growing body of evidence suggests that the opportunities for companies that adopt a supply circle mind-set and practices are real—and large. Our research indicates that the savings in materials alone could exceed USD

EXHIBIT 4

Products, components, and materials can be looped back into the value chain

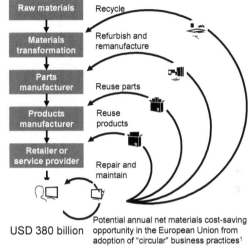

Value is created by looping products, components, and materials back into the value chain after they fulfill their utility over the life cycle of a product

USD 380 billion — Potential annual net materials cost-saving opportunity in the European Union from adoption of "circular" business practices[1]

1 For complex durables with medium life spans, based on current total input costs per sector; represents transitional scenarios for 27 EU economies
SOURCE: Ellen MacArthur Foundation, Towards the Circular Economy: Economic and business rationale for an accelerated transition, January 2012

1 trillion a year by 2025.[12] And in the European Union alone, the annual savings for durable products with moderate life spans could reach USD 630 billion—of which USD 200 billion a year could accrue to the automotive sector.[13]

But savings aren't the only benefit. Supply circle practices can also help mitigate supply risks for companies. If applied to steel consumption in the automotive, machining, and transport sectors, supply circle optimization could achieve global net materials savings equivalent to 110 million to 170 million metric tons of iron ore per year in 2025. This achievement could reduce demand-driven price volatility in these industries through

---

12 Ellen MacArthur Foundation, *Towards the Circular Economy: Accelerating the scale-up across global supply chains,* 2014, Volume 3, p. 6.
13 Ellen MacArthur Foundation, *Towards the Circular Economy: Accelerating the scale-up across global supply chains,* 2014, Volume 3, p. 20.

refurbishment and reuse, given that steel is already being recycled efficiently at a large scale.

Finally, under the right conditions, supply circle practices could become a tangible driver of global industrial innovation, job creation, and growth for the 21st century. For example, by some estimates, the remanufacturing and recycling industries already account for about one million jobs in Europe and the United States. We see signs that a supply circle approach could increase local employment, especially in entry-level and semiskilled jobs, thus addressing a serious issue facing many developed countries.

The as yet untapped potential is huge for companies in a broad range of industries. For instance[14]:

- In the global fast-moving consumer goods industry, about 80 percent of the USD 3.2 trillion worth of materials used each year is not recovered.
- In the United States, less than one-third of the rubble generated during the construction and demolition of buildings is recycled or reused—even though it contains high concentrations of recyclable steel, wood, and concrete.
- Only three dollars' worth of gold, silver, and palladium can currently be extracted from a mobile phone that, when new, contains 16 dollars' worth of these raw materials.
- In the global paper recycling industry, the difficulty of removing inks, fillers, and coatings from paper without degrading it results in a loss of materials worth USD 32 billion a year.

Where is your company on the supply circle?

Where a company is located on its industry's supply circle makes a big difference in how it's affected by resource constraints and what actions will best enable it to enhance resource productivity in its operations as

---

14   Ellen MacArthur Foundation, *Towards the Circular Economy: Accelerating the scale-up across global supply chains,* 2014, Volume 3, pp. 43 – 44.

EXHIBIT 5

Position on the supply circle affects approaches to resource-productivity improvement

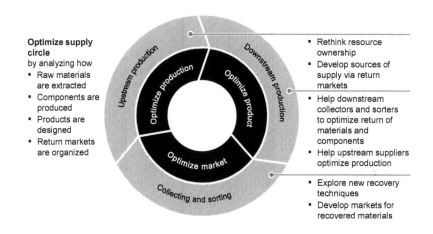

Optimize supply
circle
by analyzing how
- Raw materials
  are extracted
- Components are
  produced
- Products are
  designed
- Return markets
  are organized

- Rethink resource
  ownership
- Develop sources of
  supply via return
  markets

- Help downstream
  collectors and sorters
  to optimize return of
  materials and
  components
- Help upstream suppliers
  optimize production

- Explore new recovery
  techniques
- Develop markets for
  recovered materials

SOURCE: McKinsey Resource-Productive Operations service line

well as create more value in the overall supply circle (Exhibit 5). The main positions on the supply circle are upstream production, downstream production, and collection and sorting (waste management).

Upstream manufacturers

Upstream manufacturing companies are focused primarily on transforming materials into inputs used by other companies. Examples include refining, steel, chemicals, paper, smelting, and certain product ranges from pharmaceutical (such as active pharmaceutical ingredients) and consumer goods (for instance, beer) companies. Such manufacturers' operations are often as much as ten times more energy intensive than the operations of the companies that use their products.

Upstream manufacturers primarily concentrate on transforming products using energy while delivering semifinished products to

A case in point: The ULCOS consortium

The Ultra-Low CO_2 Steel (ULCOS) consortium is the largest initiative in the worldwide steel industry seeking solutions to the impact of global warming. The consortium's expertise includes steel making, biomass production, and geological CO_2 storage, as well as process science, engineering, energy economics, and climate change. The ULCOS partners fund 60 percent of the EUR 75 million budget. The European Commission contributes the remaining 40 percent through its Research, Technological Development, and Demonstration (RTD) framework and Research Fund Coal Steel (RFCS) programs. Both programs promote industrial research and technological development within Europe.

Since its inception in 2004, the ULCOS program has carried out considerable research. An initial feasibility study investigated more than 80 technologies, several of which were seen as offering possible breakthroughs in clean steel making. ULCOS selected and tested a number of process concepts—such as changes to blast furnace and smelting operations—that could lead to a reduction of CO_2 emissions by more than half compared with the current best practice. These concepts are being implemented in working steel plants during a phase of the project slated to run from 2010 through 2015. Results look promising. For example, pilot studies at ArcelorMittal using top gas recycling achieved a 10 to 20 percent reduction in energy consumption and a 50-plus percent reduction in CO_2 emissions versus benchmarked blast furnace processes.

Sources:

- European Commission/ CORDIS, "ULCOS: Ultra-low carbon dioxide steelmaking," *cordis.europa.eu, last modified June 27, 2012, http://cordis. europa.eu/estep/ulcos_en.html*

- Birat, Jean-Pierre: "ULCOS: The Steel Sector's Solutions to Exhibit Low-Carbon Production Routes," World Materials Perspective: The First International Summit by MATERALIA, Nancy, France, March 30 to 31, 2011, p. 10.

downstream players. They constitute the more energy-intensive part of the cycle. And because they make commodities, they are often squeezed between the owners of the resources and the downstream players. Therefore, they have the most to gain by reducing the amount of material or energy they use in production.

For this reason, to enhance resource productivity, they should start by optimizing production. This can be done in many different ways, for example, using resources more efficiently, extracting more value from resources, or using lower-quality inputs to reduce their cost position. As a second step, they can improve their waste recovery efforts, which can enable them to secure access to materials through activities such as recycling and reuse.

Downstream manufacturers

Downstream manufacturing companies focus on making components or final products by recombining semifinished products from upstream manufacturers. Examples include automotive component manufacturers, automotive OEMs, makers of certain products from chemical and pharmaceutical companies, consumer goods manufacturers, and makers of appliances and consumer electronics. Their operations are not as energy intensive as those of upstream players, and most of their yield losses have to do with physical losses that come with processes such as cutting and grinding. These companies are in direct contact with the customer and can use branding to protect their margins, though even those may be destabilized by volatility and uncertainty in resource availability and prices when companies cannot pass price swings on to the end customer fast enough or when their offerings become commoditized.

Thus, downstream companies can best begin enhancing their resource productivity by designing their products with an eye towards using materials more efficiently or creating new business models. When it comes to product strategies, they will gain the most by designing offerings to reduce material requirements, minimize energy consumed during the use of the products, drive new business through additional maintenance or service upgrades provided during the life cycle of the product, and eventually ensure that products can be recycled or reused at the end of this life cycle.

To illustrate, automobile manufacturers could design a car that uses less metal and incorporates recycled materials and that extends the life of the car or maximizes its fuel efficiency. For example, BMW is working towards a recycling target level of 85 percent and a recovery target level of 95 percent by 2015.[15] Nearly 90 percent of a Volvo truck is recycled, and about one-third of the materials used in new models (measured by weight) come from recycled materials.[16] Automakers could also produce cars in ways that consume less energy and other resources. And they could create modular designs that make it easy to substitute new parts or systems for those that break or wear out so that the vehicle owner doesn't have to scrap the entire car. These models seems counterintuitive at first glance, because revenue from new car sales would decrease. However, the model has the benefit of requiring less capital because fewer assembly lines are required. It could therefore create a better return on invested capital—which is a better proxy for shareholder value than sales or revenue.

As for new business models, companies can adopt new maintenance service approaches, where spare parts are used to generate profit. They could also charge a higher price for the initial product, with some money returned to the customer when materials are returned or recycled. Such models reduce capital-expenditure requirements. Innovative business models aimed at customers can also help—such as moving from selling products to selling services. Renting high-end appliances such as washing machines to customers, rather than selling them serves as a good example. Indeed, research from the Ellen MacArthur Foundation suggests that leasing high-end washing machines for use in homes would lower the cost of use for customers by one-third over five years. During that time, manufacturers would earn roughly one-third more in profits because they could lease their fleets of machines multiple times before refurbishment. Over a

---

15 BMW Group, "Vehicle Recycling. Focusing on Sustainability," 2009, *http://www.bmw. com/com/en/owners/service/_shared/pdf/2009_recycling.pdf.*

16 Volvo Trucks, "Materials and recycling," *volvotrucks.com*, 2012, *http://www.volvotrucks.com/trucks/global/en-gb/values/environment/our-trucks-and-services/pages/materials-and-recycling.aspx.*

20-year period, replacing the purchases of five 2,000-cycle machines with leases to one 10,000-cycle machine would yield almost 180 kilogram of steel savings and more than 2,5 tons of CO_2 savings.[17] Such approaches could also help companies tap into new segments of customers who can't afford to buy the product outright but could afford to rent it (as with car leasing).

Moreover, such companies can look beyond their own organizational boundaries to help their suppliers—upstream manufacturers—improve their own resource productivity. For example, upstream players that are in the commodity market can develop more complex products and lock in their customers with specific grades that their competitors cannot match. Downstream companies can use their purchasing power to help suppliers locate more sustainable sourcing options for raw materials and make more efficient use of energy resources, such as purchasing electricity jointly. In this way, downstream players can help their suppliers become more cost-competitive so that their cost of goods sold goes down, which will ultimately lower purchasing prices.

Collection and sorting (waste management) companies

Collection and sorting enterprises handle waste materials—this entails collecting, processing, and managing waste. These companies can benefit strongly from resource constraints, because their core business—waste handling—can create additional margin through smart collection and sorting of the valuable resources contained in the waste.

Consequently, such companies can best enhance resource productivity and the supply circle by optimizing their collecting and sorting processes and developing new markets for material reuse. For instance, using recycled glass reduces the cost of producing glass for downstream manufacturers and offers an economically viable option for collection and sorting companies. Examples of this can be found in the higher glass recycling rates, which can exceed 90 percent, with waste companies earning a good margin. To benefit from these opportunities and open up resource

---

17   Ellen MacArthur Foundation, *Towards the Circular Economy: Accelerating the scale-up across global supply chains*, 2014, Volume 3, p. 6.

A case in point: Ricoh's GreenLine brand

Ricoh, a global maker of office machines, designed its GreenLine brand of office copiers and printers to maximize the reusability of products and components while minimizing the use of virgin materials. Products returning from Ricoh's leasing contracts are inspected, dismantled, and taken through an extensive refurbishing process that includes replacing components and updating software before the machines reenter the market.

GreenLine products are now offered in six major European markets, where they account for 10 to 20 percent of Ricoh's sales by volume. What is Impressive is that they earn margins two times higher than those of the company's comparable new products—without a reduction in quality.

For products that cannot be remanufactured, refurbished, or upgraded, Ricoh harvests the components and recycles them at local facilities. The company is considering returning some recycled materials to its manufacturing plants in Asia for production of new components. Ricoh estimates it could save up to 30 percent on the cost of materials for such components. Overall, the company says that it's on track to reduce the input of new resources in its products by 25 percent below its 2007 levels no later than 2020.

Source:
Ricoh, *GreenLine brochure, 2011, http://www.ricoh-europe.com/ Images/Greenline%20brochure%20 A5_N_19April2012_t_57-37302.pdf.*

streams, waste management companies should be able to create markets by carefully aligning all stakeholders, such as the public, government agencies, and businesses. Ideas for fostering such alignment include the joint development of recycling programs where industry and government agencies join forces to explain to stakeholders why sorting is required and how can it be done.

For instance, in 2011, McKinsey and Veolia Water established a joint venture to establish a new business model aimed at opening up a USD

500 billion market for water and piloted the effort in New York City. The companies proposed working with the New York City Department of Environmental Protection and the New York City Water Board to develop innovative ways to serve municipal water utilities, to identify and implement operational expense (energy, chemicals) savings of over USD 100 million per year from a total operations and maintenance budget of USD 1.2 billion, and to help publicly run water utilities improve their profitability. McKinsey and Veolia are seeking to roll out the joint venture to additional cities in the United States, with the goal of ultimately rolling it out globally.[18]

Collection and sorting companies should also develop the sorting and collection technologies and capabilities necessary to mine the highest-value materials from the general waste stream at the lowest possible cost. The good news is that major organizational and technological advances have been achieved in presorting, sorting, organics processing, and waste-to-energy conversion. By exploiting these advances, waste management companies can recover much more material than they can with older systems, and they can produce higher-quality recyclates. They can also sort large volumes of varied waste, separating the valuable materials from the less valuable ones. And they can adjust their sorting criteria to optimize selection based on scrap values in the spot market.

Moreover, waste management companies can develop innovative business models to help other companies with their material-sourcing and reuse strategies. For instance, they could develop logistical solutions that enable manufacturers to capture value from waste materials left over after production or after a product has reached the end of its life cycle. In addition, they can transform themselves from waste operators into raw materials and energy suppliers, in part by advising other companies on how to design products that can more readily be recycled and reused.

Consider Waste Management, which was able to help one of its customers, Alcoa, collect and reuse a raw material called aluminum oxide—a

---

18 Veolia, "New York City's Big Numbers," *veoliawaterna.com*, December 2011, http://www.veoliawaterna.com/media/newsletters/2011-december/nyc-water-dep-savings-plan/.

A case in point: Veolia Environnement

The French company Veolia Environnement offers customized services in water management, energy management, and waste management. The company takes a three-pronged approach on behalf of its clients: moderation (avoiding unnecessary consumption), efficiency (effective use of resources), and the use of renewable materials and energies.

Veolia's Environmental Services division operates across the waste management sector, developing and offering clients innovative, high-performance technologies to produce more new resources from waste and energy recovery processes covering a wide range of activities. All of these recovery processes contribute to saving raw materials in a world where natural resources are becoming increasingly scarce.

Waste recovery technologies are also implemented in all of the group's divisions. Veolia Water, for example, has produced 0.8 million megawatt-hours of electrical and thermal energy through wastewater treatment and sewage sludge recycling. The division constantly seeks new solutions for resource conservation. Its goal is to "refine" wastewater into various sources of energy (biofuels, methane, hydrogen, and ethanol), organic and mineral ingredients (fertilizers), and biomaterials, such as the biopolymer PHA (polyhydroxyalkanoates), which can be converted into bioplastics.

In 2011, Veolia Environmental Services recovered 40.4 million metric tons of waste in the form of materials and energy and produced 8.9 million mega-watt-hours of electrical and thermal energy. Veolia Environnement plans to increase production of renewable energy from waste to 10 percent and to achieve an overall level of materials recovery of 26 percent by 2014.[19]

---

19   Waste Management, "One Mission. Many Solutions," *wm.com*, 2014, http://www.wm.com/ thinkgreen/case-studies.jsp.

fine, powdery substance that Alcoa workers, unable to reuse, routinely swept up and threw away. Instead, Waste Management developed a system to reclaim 20 to 25 tons per week, reducing landfill waste and generating an annual savings of USD 500,000.[20]

Dispelling myths about resource-productive operations

Companies may be intrigued by the potential benefits of enhancing resource productivity by adopting supply circle practices. But persistent myths about resource productivity—many of them regarding energy efficiency—have discouraged numerous companies from exploring this possibility more closely. Below, we examine—and dispel—some of the more common myths. Executives and change leaders should pay close attention whenever they hear any of the statements listed below, because they indicate a mindset that will only block further improvement in resource productivity.

Myth 1: "Energy is cheap"

Energy may be cheap relative to other costs, such as labor and raw materials. But in many industries, energy costs constitute a sizable portion of companies' profit-and-loss statements—even in countries with relatively low energy rates. For instance, in regions characterized by high labor costs, even with low prices (gas costing EUR 3 per gigajoule, electricity at EUR 40 per megawatt-hour), the energy to power a hot strip steel mill producing 4 million metric tons of steel per year still represents a cost three times greater than that of direct labor. And the cost is one-and-a-half times greater than maintenance labor and direct labor combined. Even in industries where energy is a smaller portion of the cost structure (for example, groceries), achieving a savings in energy efficiency can have a dramatic effect on overall margins.

Our response: Don't look at price–look at cost. Rather than regarding energy as a relatively unimportant cost, companies need to view their annual energy cost as a variable cost—one that they can reduce by up to 15 percent.

---

20   Waste Management, "Alcoa Case Study," *wm.com,* 2014, https://www.wm.com/sustainability-services/documents/case-studies/Alcoa%20Case%20Study.pdf.

Myth 2: "Resource-productivity investments have a long payback period"

Many operations executives assume that enhancing resource productivity is all about firing a "silver bullet" at the problem. They imagine that a large capital expenditure to fund new or upgraded equipment or facilities is necessary. Consequently, they worry that the payback period for such a hefty investment will be too lengthy, and they hesitate to make the investment.

We don't think of resource-productivity investments as a silver bullet but as "silver buckshot" comprising many small, relatively low capital-expenditure initiatives that collectively lead to good savings. For instance, if 100 energy-saving initiatives each reduces energy costs by 0.3 percent, the collective savings would be 30 percent. The idea of tiny slices of savings adding up to significant ones may be difficult to grasp for some people—but it's an important one. And the payback period can be less than two years for the majority of initiatives. The choice of metrics and implementation tracking is very important here, because the hoped-for payback is never achieved if people focus on the wrong metrics or do not consequently track progress. Examples include the cost of water. Water itself is cheap, but what gets lost through water use—energy and raw materials—is expensive.

Our response: Think silver buckshot, not silver bullet. Rather than expecting one large capital expenditure to deliver major gains in resource productivity, companies can design multiple small initiatives that collectively deliver a major gain.

Myth 3: "Energy is not core to our operations"

As a significant cost, energy expended on core and noncore activities deserves the same attention as that expended on other topics such as quality and production scheduling. Yet even when energy makes up 10 percent of total costs, companies often outsource management of energy to utility or facility providers. We've seen that the companies that benefit most from energy efficiency tend to manage energy use with a clear demarcation of responsibility within the organization. Even if they do outsource, these companies ensure that efficiency-improvement goals are part of the provider's contract, and they reject high fixed-cost items such as perpetuity on grid installation cost. Moreover, they tackle energy-efficiency issues in activities supporting their core processes (such as cooling water systems, compressed air, and production pumps), which often make up about 30 percent of their total energy bill.

Our response: Designate clear responsibility for managing total energy efficiency. Companies need to put in place the right in-house organization structure and detail clear responsibilities for all energy use—in core and noncore activities alike. Moreover, they must actively manage their own energy use, whether they outsource or not.

Myth 4: "Energy impact cannot be measured and managed"

Managers often express concern about the number of meters they might need to install throughout a manufacturing plant to see the impact of any improvements in energy efficiency. But a good performance-measurement system built on the proper set of indicators and supported with regular performance meetings is fundamental to success.

One way to think about key performance indicators (KPIs) is to understand the different types and define a mix of KPIs for energy efficiency. For example, a leading KPI is one that operators can act upon on an ongoing basis, such as temperature ranges or concentrations. In contrast, a lagging KPI is something that managers review at the end of a shift, day, or month, such as gigajoule per metric ton or megawatt-hours consumed during downtimes. Leveling indicators, on the other hand, operate over a longer time horizon given that they report a gradual deterioration of equipment, such as seawater pump efficiency.

Carefully chosen leading KPIs for processes help shop-floor managers and employees to continuously monitor and improve their plant's energy efficiency. Lagging and leveling KPIs are helpful for senior management—but lagging KPIs must first be normalized for process factors that have high energy impact, such as product mix, production speed, and equipment availability (downtime of the line). For instance, reducing the production rate of a cement mill by 10 percent leads to about a 10 percent increase in kilowatt-hours per ton of cement, and changing the cement type often has an even larger impact. The purpose of normalization is two-fold. First, it helps to ensure that lagging KPIs are meaningful and that managers can use them to assess whether a process is performing well in regard to resources.

Our response: Manage for performance. Instead of focusing on measuring energy usage, companies should manage operations for energy efficiency. This should be done by using a blend of leading, lagging, and leveling KPIs normalized to their production activity.

Myth 5: "Our yield cannot be further improved"

Many companies believe that they have already optimized yield for a particular process as much as possible, and that there's nothing more they can do to improve yield further, except for a technology change. Yet a manufacturer can identify yield-maximization opportunities within current technology by combining first-order control parameters, which relate to the quantity of incoming raw materials (such as how much the company produces per unit of throughput of raw materials), with second-order parameters, which relate to processes and equipment (such as reflux rate or pump speed or rotations per minute), and even third-order parameters such as resulting pressures in a reactor vessel or outside temperature.

By examining the intersections of first-, second-, and third-order parameters, managers can gather more data and thus gain more insights into factors influencing yield—such as how flow in a particular scrubber affects output quality. Additionally, this deeper understanding of operational parameters with their associated losses can lead to minor upgrades to current technology. For example, consider a chemical player that found out that coproduct absorption was a third-order parameter that had a strong negative effect on performance. It focused on finding ways to make small capital upgrades to the absorption system and was able to improve yield. (Companies that don't have measurement mechanisms in place are unable to take advantage of this kind of opportunity.)

Likewise, examining the intersection of processes between organization functions can generate additional ideas for maximizing yield. Take raw materials procurement. By optimizing the procurement price and including the added value of the different elements in the raw materials in the production process and even in the sales of by-products, a company can improve its raw materials mix in ways that increase overall profit per hour. For example, in the steel industry, the production of steel is a process involving transforming coal into coke and turning iron ore fines into sinter; both combine with pulverized coal injection (PCI) pellets and lump in the blast furnace to produce liquid iron, which is then processed in the steel shop to become steel. Decisions in regard to the quality of the raw materials purchased will affect all four steps, and producers have to make trade-offs among throughput, overall cost, and stability of the local operation. For instance, using cheaper coking coal reduces the unit cost of coke but can reduce the strength and size distribution of the coke produced. As a result, permeability in the blast furnace will be decreased, which in its turn will reduce the throughput rate of the blast furnace and the amount of PCI (cheaper coal than coking coal) that can be used to displace coke. Additional effects are the potential reduction of coke-oven gas recovered owing to the cheaper coal or the introduction of sulfur that will require additional processing in the steel shop.

Our response: Look deeper for opportunities. By using data analytics and advanced modeling techniques to uncover the more complex relationships between parameters and functional processes, companies can find additional opportunities to increase yield beyond what they have already accomplished.

Capturing the resource-productivity prize: Five core beliefs

Combating the impact of persistent myths about resource productivity and supply chains isn't easy. Companies need to embed new ways of thinking—core beliefs— in their management teams, workforces, and organizational cultures. We use the word belief because it conveys the notion that making this change is about more than using new tools; it's about perceiving reality and thinking about production in a whole new way—in other words, adopting a radically different mind-set.

The approach that McKinsey has developed for enhancing resource productivity is guided by five core beliefs: think lean, think limits, think profit per hour, think holistic, and think circular (Exhibit 6). In the sections that follow, we take a closer look at each of these beliefs.

Exhibit 6

EXHIBIT 6

Five core beliefs are critical for enhancing resource productivity

Build resource-productivity improvements on top of traditional lean thinking	Stretch your aspirations by using the theoretical-limit concept	Prioritize profit as the main factor for final decisions	Involve the whole organization to sustain change	Move from finite supply chains to supply circles
1	2	3	4	5
Think lean Lean and green are highly synergistic and use the same fundamentals	**Think limits** Use theoretical limits to set ambitious goals that foster creative thinking and deliver breakthrough impact	**Think profit per hour** Drive sustainable profit by understanding the relationships among throughput, yield, energy, and the environment	**Think holistic** Reinforce the benefits from technical improvements by improving and tailoring management systems and mindsets and behaviors	**Think circular** Boost business opportunities and competitive advantages by optimizing across product and service life cycles

SOURCE: McKinsey Resource-Productive Operations service line

Think lean

Thinking lean in the context of resource productivity is all about building resource-productivity improvements on top of traditional lean thinking, which focuses on labor and asset productivity. Lean and resource productivity are highly synergistic and utilize the same fundamentals. Thus, companies don't need to reinvent the wheel when it comes to designing resource-productivity initiatives. Instead, they can extend core concepts from lean, such as analysis of losses of anything that does not add value for the customer and relentless waste reduction, adapting these concepts to the resource-productivity approach as needed. For instance, when they use the lean tool MIFA (material information flow analysis), they can add energy to what they are analyzing. In other words, they can look at their manufacturing operations through the "lens" of lean but change the color of the lens to resource productivity.

For example, a large refinery's lean program evolved into a "lean and green" program when the program managers added resource-productivity tools to the lean toolbox and used the fundamental principle of removing waste. The refinery uncovered savings of 3 percent in variable costs without having to make any additional capital expenditures.

Think limits

Thinking limits centers on stretching aspirations by deploying the theoretical-limit concept, which sets ambitious goals that are free from the influence of incremental bottom-up ideas (Exhibit 7). Theoretical limits establish the value-added amount of energy and raw materials that reach the customer; that is, only the energy and raw materials required to generate the final product based on the laws of thermodynamics and physics in a 100 percent efficient stoichiometric conversion. Companies can use theoretical limits to set enterprising goals that foster creative thinking and deliver breakthrough impact.

For instance, managers can ask themselves how much energy or material is required for a particular manufacturing process theoretically,

Exhibit 7

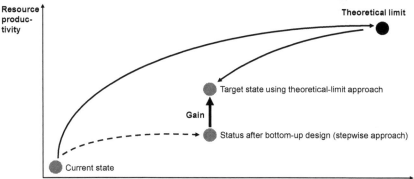

EXHIBIT 7

The theoretical-limit concept drives ideas for enhancing resource productivity

Resource productivity

Theoretical limit

Target state using theoretical-limit approach

Gain

Status after bottom-up design (stepwise approach)

Current state

Transition

Theoretical limit stretches our thinking by setting ambitious goals that are free from the influence of incremental bottom-up ideas

SOURCE: McKinsey Resource-Productive Operations service line

what maximum amount of energy and materials can be recovered, how much of a particular material is required on a stoichiometric basis, and what kinetic and thermodynamic quantities of energy go into the product or are required to overcome the activation energy barrier and start the reaction. Often, more energy is required than initially expected, because reactions start only when an energy barrier (the activation energy) has been crossed. (For example, a match doesn't burn by itself, although, based on thermodynamics, it should. You need to start the reaction by giving it some extra energy: striking the match to a box.) Such analysis sets the boundaries of the potential improvement opportunity and generates insights that managers can use to define process-improvement solutions. It also helps managers establish a solid monetary base to start from.

To illustrate, in membrane-chlorine analysis, about 70 percent of all electrical power (both potential and current) goes into the product and therefore can never be reduced when using technology that relies on the standard process based on the following reaction:

$$2NaCl + 2H_2O -> Cl_2 + H_2 + 2NaOH \quad E0 = 2.2V$$

Changing the reaction and associated technology can, of course, change the game completely. For example, Bayer[21] invented oxygen depolarized cathode technology, which reinvented the Cl_2 production process according to the fuel cell principle so that it consumes 30 percent less electricity. Notably, the process no longer produces H_2. This is because the H_2 is used to reduce the required potential and will be consumed to become water.

One steel company used the energy theoretical-limit method to identify a gap of up to 50 percent between current resource consumption and the limit of its reheating furnaces at the hot strip mill. Notably, one-third of the gap came from operational losses (where no capital expenditure was necessary), and two-thirds came from equipment design.

Think profit per hour

Thinking profit per hour focuses on prioritizing profit as the main factor for final decisions about resource-productivity enhancement efforts. Companies

---

21   Bayer, "Oxygen depolarized cathode technology for energy-efficient chlorine production," *bayer.com*, August 12, 2014, http://www.bayer.com/en/chlorine-production.aspx.

EXHIBIT 8

Profit per hour drives maximum value from operations

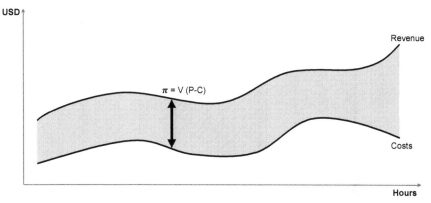

Profit per hour allows us to analyze the impact that resource-
productivity initiatives have on both revenue and costs

SOURCE: McKinsey Resource-Productive Operations service line

should review the full profit equation—revenue minus costs—when making operational changes aimed at improving resource productivity (Exhibit 8). They should also weigh the trade-offs involved, among factors such as throughput, yield, energy consumption, and impact on the environment, considering how changes in regard to one of these might affect the others.

This approach places all variable costs together, shows clear variability in processes, and provides a clear line of sight into the links connecting functions such as procurement, production, and sales. It also includes overall equipment effectiveness (OEE, a standard lean metric indicating an asset's productivity) by focusing on the number of good quality production hours (time spent making products that can be sold directly to the consumers who ordered them so that no rework or downgrades are required) per year that a company achieves.

For example, a company in a process industry reprioritized a business unit's product portfolio by profit per hour instead of profit per ton. The result was a 2 percent increase in both gross and contribution margin (Exhibit 9).

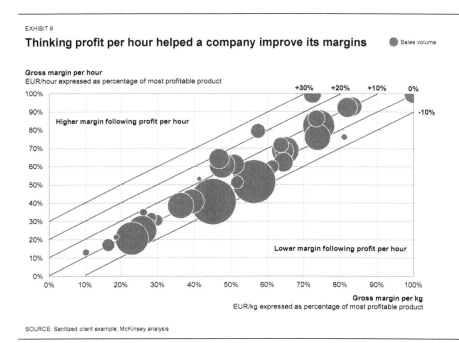

EXHIBIT 9

Thinking profit per hour helped a company improve its margins ⚫ Sales volume

Gross margin per hour
EUR/hour expressed as percentage of most profitable product

SOURCE: Sanitized client example; McKinsey analysis

Think holistic

Thinking holistic is about involving the entire organization in implementing and sustaining the changes a company has made to improve resource productivity. The most-effective companies know that making their resources more productive involves much more than just modifying the technical infrastructure driving their operations. They know how important it is to make alterations in their management infrastructure (including organization structures and performance-management systems) and their people infrastructure (fostering a new mind-set and behaviors and strengthening capabilities). Only by doing both can they reinforce the technical changes they want to make.

One chemical company broadened its approach to sustainability by setting the right targets using load curves, a technique used to normalize energy performance for changes in production speed and to gain a clear view of an asset's and work crew's performance vis-a-vis specific energy consumption. The company also invested heavily in changing mind-sets, capabilities, and behaviors through brainstorming sessions, sitewide communication, training sessions, and a clear capability-improvement plan. The program proved so successful that the sites involved were able to qualify for ISO 50001 Energy Management Systems certification soon after implementing the changes.

Think circular

Thinking circular centers on making the mind shift from linear, finite supply chains to supply circles, as discussed previously. Companies that master this way of thinking consider their products to be their future resources and collaborate internally and externally to optimize their industry's overall supply circle.

To help companies transform the five core beliefs into practices that generate measurable results, we and our colleagues at McKinsey has developed a comprehensive set of proprietary tools that are already enabling companies to reduce their resource consumption, decrease the unit price of resources, and optimize their product mix and pricing. Each chapter in Section II of this book explores a core belief in detail; explains which tools to use, and when and how, to enable the practices associated with that belief; and provides a case study illustrating how the tools can be deployed and what kinds of benefits companies can gain from using them.

***

Enhancing resource productivity requires new behaviors, new processes, new organization structures, and new ways of interacting with other organizations. None of these changes can take place unless manufacturing executives and managers alter the way they think—about resources, about how supplies of resources flow within their industry, and about how much improvement is possible in their use of resources. Only by changing the way they think can manufacturers overcome the limiting effect of common myths about resource productivity. To think in a decidedly different way, companies must adopt the five core beliefs. Those that manage this transformation will lay the groundwork for deploying a comprehensive set of tools and techniques that will help them extract more value from the resources they use and achieve significant savings that will go straight to the bottom line.

A comprehensive resource productivity toolkit

A Reduce resource consumption

1 Resource value stream mapping Map and quantify resources as they flow through each step in system	2 Technical map Discover key technical parameters and overall system control logic	3 Waste walk and resource-loss framework Identify resource losses from waste, variability, and inflexibility	4 Loss bridge and theoretical limit Identify minimum theoretical level of resource consumption	5 Load curve (including time evolution) Quantify performance losses on equipment, process, and production
6 Cost curve Quantify losses due to resource demand/supply mismatch (e.g., cooling systems)	7 Network map and loss analysis Map and quantify losses in makeup distribution networks (e.g., compressed air)	8 Resource-life-cycle analysis Identify losses in the life cycle for each type of energy or resource	9 Temperature mapping and pinch analysis Quantify losses due to suboptimal reuse of heat (e.g., heating network)	10 Process parameter analysis[22] Quantify profit losses due to suboptimal control of key parameters
11 Value-at-stake analysis Identify the resource impact of 1% change in yield and throughput	12 Yield-driver tree Identify and improve the main drivers that influence yield	13 Machine system analysis Prioritize motors, pumps, and fans for quantification of losses due to inefficiencies	14 Shutdown analysis Identify resource consumption during shutdowns and idle times	15 Consumption and inventory analysis Analyze resource-consumption drivers for goods in stock

B Reduce unit price of resources

1 Utility and resource contract baseline/matrix Develop resource matrix using existing contracts and pricing for current resources being consumed	2 Resource-sourcing analysis Analyze resource usage and sourcing strategies (e.g., value-in-use, supplier substitutes, fuel flexibility)	3 Negotiation fact base Develop financial negotiation fact base across multiple suppliers to increase leverage	4 Contract strategy Structure contracts to maximize lifetime value of resource

C Optimize mix or improve price

1 Product sales and margin baseline Understand products by sales, margins, profit per hour, specifications, and quality compared with competition	2 Pricing analysis Analyze how sustainability-related production affects customers' willingness to pay	3 Product mix and capacity-demand analysis Determine product mix that will meet market demands and maximize operational capabilities	4 Now-market research Build understanding of sustainability-related opportunities in new market segments and regions

Goal: maximize profit per hour by stretching towards theoretical limit

---

22   The process parameter analysis tool can be used to do the following:
A) reduce resource consumption; B) reduce unit price of resources; and C) optimize mix or improve price.

Part 2

FIVE CORE BELIEFS

A more successful approach to resource productivity will require more than simply purchasing new technology. In fact, major capital expenditures should be far down on the list of potential solutions. Instead, companies must fundamentally change the way they think about the issue of resource productivity. Drawing on our experience with a range of companies, we think this comes down to embracing five critical beliefs: think lean, think limits, think profit per hour, think holistic, and think circular.

CHAPTER 3

THINK LEAN

*T*o make optimal resource-productivity decisions, companies need a thorough understanding of how their production processes consume resources and where that consumption can be improved. Lean is a potent and proven method that provides that understanding. Made famous by the Toyota production system, lean is a rigorous methodology that focuses on reducing waste and loss. Lean, in its classic product-oriented application, begins by defining the value that customers are willing to pay for and then stringently applies tools and techniques to eradicate all steps, features, and processes that don't add to that value. In the resource-productivity version, companies analyze a process and apply similar tools and techniques to eliminate all sources of waste.

A risky situation

Resource productivity is a rapidly evolving discipline, and new technologies and approaches are emerging at every turn. Because resource productivity is fast moving, companies often tackle its challenges by trying to leverage the latest solutions. However, many deploy these solutions without a comprehensive and systematic understanding of where the greatest opportunities lie. As a result, improvement efforts often fall short of expectations.

Installation of variable frequency drives (VFDs) is a prime example. VFDs control the speed of an AC motor by varying the frequency of the power source. Attaching a VFD to a pump in order to vary its speed is a common practice. However, if the need is to slow the pump speed because too much water is moving through all points in the process, installing a VFD may be overkill. The device adds maximum value when different water flows are needed at varying points in the process. If the water flow need is static, a smaller pump may provide a much better return on investment.

Companies do more than miss opportunities by deploying new technologies too quickly. When building new manufacturing plants, for example, organizations will often invest in power plants with capacities that greatly exceed what is needed—the excess power likely fuels energy-inefficient equipment. Lean thinking is a powerful tool for addressing this problem.

A closer look at lean

Lean originated in the Japanese auto industry shortly after World War II. In response to postwar resource constraints, Japanese automakers developed highly efficient production methods with a pronounced emphasis on meeting specific customer needs as quickly and efficiently as possible. The term lean was coined in the 1980s by two Massachusetts Institute of Technology scholars, James Womack and Daniel Jones. They spent several years studying the production processes of Japanese automakers to discover what led to their success. Womack and Jones gleaned several principles that underpinned the success of Japanese carmakers vis-a-vis their US counterparts.

Lean does more with less by delivering exactly the right product, in the right quantity, and at the right time. The concept of a value stream lies at the heart of that ability. The value stream identifies all the activities and information in a production process that adds value for customers. It also targets activities that don't add value and need to be eliminated. With a mind-set that thrives on eliminating waste, managers practicing lean strive to create an efficient just-in-time process flow that includes only those steps that add value.

Since the 1980s, lean has become a mainstay of manufacturing. In recent years, however, it has made significant inroads into services, IT, product development, and healthcare. Business leaders concerned about natural resources are also taking up the mantle. Using lean principles, they have been able to make significant improvements in the resource productivity of their operations.

Making resource productivity a pillar of a company's lean production system offers distinct advantages. The application of well-known lean principles to resource productivity, including standardization and continuous improvement, utilizes concepts that a broad base of managers and internal change agents are already familiar with. In addition, best practices such as performance meetings and integrated key performance indicators (KPIs) are already likely in place and translate easily to resource-productivity endeavors. Furthermore, frontline employees will be familiar with the lean message and receptive to applying it to improve resource usage.

A lean lens on resource losses

Applying lean principles to resource productivity is based on identifying the three primary sources of loss that erode operational and energy performance: inflexibility, variability, and waste (Exhibit 10). Each of these impinges on the system's ability to deliver the desired quality or service level at an optimal cost.

Exhibit 10

EXHIBIT 10

Inflexibility, variability, and waste erode operational and resource performance

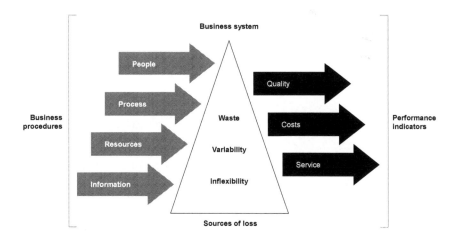

SOURCE: McKinsey Resource-Productive Operations service line

By applying the three sources of loss from lean to resource productivity, companies can create a systemic view of what causes material, water, or energy loss; how and where. That understanding, in turn, helps pinpoint where solutions will have the greatest impact.

Resource-productivity loss: Inflexibility

Processes are inflexible when they can't respond easily to change. Oversize production batches are an example of inflexibility in its classic application to products. For instance, if batches in a chemical production process are determined by tank size, rather than customer demand, and the need to fill them to a certain minimum level, the process will be unable to respond quickly to changes in market demand.

Lean can also pinpoint where inflexible production processes lead to resource loss. The following examples illustrate a wide range of potential sources of loss due to inflexibility across the entire value chain.

Customer

Customer specifications for a product will usually fall along a range. If process standards are always set to meet the highest customer needs, the company will waste resources because many customers don't require that standard. Water content in paper is an example of this. Some customers are able to tolerate more water than others. If the process produces only the lowest level of water content, the business wastes energy by drying paper more than it needs to. Additionally, an expensive resource, fiber, must be used to replace the water.

Inventory

Inflexibility can also lead to unnecessary inventory loss. For example, the production process at one petrochemical plant generates two by-products of different value. Although the reactors could be adjusted to maximize the higher-value by-product, the company lacks storage for the higher-value product. As a result, the organization is forced to produce an inordinate amount of the lower-value by-product.

Production process

Inflexible production processes also drain resources unnecessarily. In an integrated steel plant, for instance, steel slabs are heated in a furnace before being fashioned into coils. When shutdowns and other issues slow the production process, many steel manufacturers don't have furnace models that adjust the heat based on different production speeds. The temperature is often set high to accommodate the fastest production pace resulting in the generation of excess heat and energy, which goes into the exhaust and out of the stack.

Production-process support

Equipment such as motors attached to a pump can also make processes inflexible. Because motors move at a fixed rate, the pump will also operate at a fixed rate, even though the production work is far from static. Pumping water at a fixed rate often creates excess that must bypass the system. This uses energy, as does the need to pressurize the water again. VFD pumps address this source of loss very well.

Buildings and environment

In an assembly line, 50 to 60 percent of energy is used to control a building's climate. Much of that is lost. Welding lines, for example, generate toxic fumes across the entire plant, even though they may account for as little as 10 percent of the space. Because the welding line isn't housed separately, the air in the entire building must be refreshed much more frequently than it would if the welders were in a separate structure.

Resource-productivity loss: Variability

Variability refers to changes within a repeating process that affect the output. In the classic product orientation of lean, companies focus their efforts on variability that affects product quality and production efficiency, such as machine breakdowns, changes in raw material quality, and inconsistent work processes. To improve resource productivity, it is often helpful to shift the focus to processes and the environment by addressing the "six M's":

- Man and management
- Method
- Material

- Machine
- Measurement
- Mother Nature.

In the pages that follow, we illustrate these through examples from steel manufacturing.

Man and management

People often introduce variation into a process, either inadvertently or through the absence of standards. For example, after a short shutdown, furnace operators may believe they need to make up for lost time and boost temperatures beyond targets to increase production speeds. In addition, managers often change targets too frequently, fail to enforce standards, and provide inconsistent feedback.

Method

Poorly designed processes can also introduce significant variability in energy use. Furnace models that don't adjust for short stops and other delays, for example, can result in product that is manufactured faster than necessary and, thus, consumes more energy than needed. Production schedules should remain as constant as possible in order to maximize energy use.

Material

There is almost always variation in materials that enter a production process, such as steel slabs moving into a furnace at different temperatures. The colder the slab, the more energy that is needed to heat it. Standardizing temperatures optimizes energy use.

Machine

Variation in the use of the same or similar equipment can increase energy costs. If a plant is operating two furnaces, loading one furnace more than the other can have an impact on performance, as one furnace may have a waste-heat exchanger to preheat incoming combustion air, and the other may not, the former is therefore more efficient.

Measurement

The absence of disciplined measurement regimens is another source of resource loss. For example, equipment operators who are concerned that pyrometers on certain furnaces are inaccurate will often set furnace temperatures higher than needed.

Mother Nature

Environmental conditions drive considerable variability. If a combustion air preheating heat exchange is too small, for example, it will consume more energy when the outside temperature is low than if the exchangers were properly sized.

Resource-productivity loss: Waste

Lean targets eight sources of waste—everything in a process that does not add to the value customers are willing to pay for (Exhibit 11).

Exhibit 11

EXHIBIT 11

A lean process targets eight types of waste

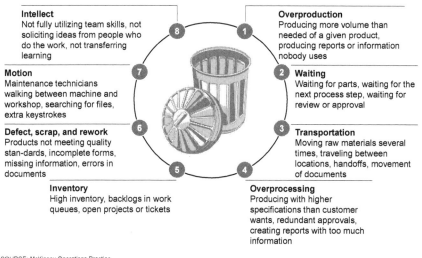

Intellect
Not fully utilizing team skills, not soliciting ideas from people who do the work, not transferring learning

Motion
Maintenance technicians walking between machine and workshop, searching for files, extra keystrokes

Defect, scrap, and rework
Products not meeting quality stan-dards, incomplete forms, missing information, errors in documents

Inventory
High inventory, backlogs in work queues, open projects or tickets

Overproduction
Producing more volume than needed of a given product, producing reports or information nobody uses

Waiting
Waiting for parts, waiting for the next process step, waiting for review or approval

Transportation
Moving raw materials several times, traveling between locations, handoffs, movement of documents

Overprocessing
Producing with higher specifications than customer wants, redundant approvals, creating reports with too much information

SOURCE: McKinsey Operations Practice

Consider overproduction. This can happen when a company produces more inventory than it can sell at a given time. Overproduction is considered the most costly source of waste. It ties up capital and incurs unnecessary transportation and warehousing costs to move and store excess inventory. In terms of resource productivity, overproduction is the creation of more utility (such as compressed air) than a company can use at a given time. For example, if a compressor is set to produce a fixed amount of compressed air over a given period of time, it will inevitably produce more than is needed at certain points. The unused air is often vented into the atmosphere; the cost to compress it is similarly lost.

Transportation is another example. From a classic lean perspective, transportation waste stems from challenges such as the need to move finished goods off site for packing. Applying an energy lens, transportation waste comes from excess energy used to move a utility through the plant. Steam, for example, must travel from the boiler to different process points that use it. If the piping has leaks or its design includes unneeded turns, the steam dissipates without ever being used.

In addition to lean's eight categories, we have identified two specific resource-productivity sources of waste. We have added them to round out the lean application to resource productivity. Inefficient equipment is the first. Many production facilities have machinery that hails from eras when energy was much less expensive or legacy machinery that's still around from previous build-outs and hasn't been upgraded. For example, factories may be using pumps that are much less efficient than similar equipment designed more recently.

System integration is another source of waste unique to resource productivity. Often, energy is put into a product only to be taken out again later in the process. For example, a product is heated with steam during production and then chilled with cooling water for storage. Each is a separate process with its own costs. To reduce waste, the finished hot product can be used to heat the cold raw material, and vice versa—provided the production processes are sufficiently integrated. Similarly, pressure residing in liquid or gas can be used through expansion turbines among other options.

Classic and resource-specific sources of waste can be targeted by lean

Waste categories and examples	Result	Operations examples
Classic		
Overproduction Producing more volume than needed of a given product or generating unnecessary reports	Producing utilities that aren't used	Excess cooling water is sent to the plant, bypasses the heat exchanger, and is sent back to the tower
Waiting Waiting for approvals, reviews, or parts needed to perform the next step of the process	Energy is consumed even during production stops	During a production stop or shutdown, conveyor belts, pumps, and fans still operate even though no product is flowing through the process
Transportation Moving raw materials repeatedly, traveling between locations and handoffs	Energy is lost during transportation	Multiple air compressors are linked to pipes that have extensive leakage or large pressure drops occur in pipe networks
Overprocessing Producing a higher-quality product than the customer is willing to pay for	Energy consumption is deliberately set higher than the process needs	Operators add a safety margin to ideal settings of furnace temperatures, production speeds, and compressed air pressure
Inventory Accumulating excess stock, work-queue backlogs, open projects and tickets	Energy is lost in stored inventory and energy required to store products	Hot steel slabs cool too much prior to production or operators must heat or cool inventory in warehouses because of overproduction
Rework and scrap Producing products that don't meet quality standards or incomplete, error-filled documents	Resources are consumed by rework or scrap production	Improperly sized sinter is sent back to the beginning of the sintering process
Motion Walking between machines and workshops or searching for needed items such as files	Processes or pieces of equipment use resources inefficiently, although the equipment is efficient	Company uses high-quality, efficient boilers, exchangers, and VFDs but sets the oxygen level too high, which reduces boiler efficiency
Employee potential Failing to fully utilize employee skills or elicit ideas from the people who do the work	Company fails to capture employee knowledge to identify and reduce energy waste	Employees are not directly involved in developing energy-saving initiatives
Resource-specific		
Efficiency Operating inefficient equipment	Higher energy use due to inefficient equipment (e.g., motors, compressors)	A boiler set to run at optimal levels loses energy because the stack lacks an economizer
Integration Failing to take advantage of available energies across different processes	Available energies (heat, cold, work, pressure) are being wasted	When products are heated for processing and cooled for storage, not using the hot product to heat nor using the cool product to chill

Cogeneration for energy integration

By using a heat and power setup, companies can reduce energy costs considerably. Take an example we've drawn from an analysis of European manufacturing operations. In this example, generating 1 megawatt-hour of low-pressure steam would typically cost EUR 32 using a boiler if we assume a fuel cost of EUR 30 per megawatt-hour and an efficiency rate of 95 percent. A heat and power setup can produce 1 megawatt-hour of low pressure steam for EUR 18 benefiting from the highly efficient gas to electricity conversion in the gas turbine and steam backpressure turbine (Exhibit 12).

Exhibit 12

EXHIBIT 12

Example of energy cost savings from cogeneration

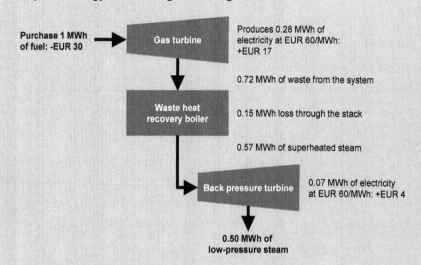

Cost of low-pressure steam is EUR 9 (= EUR 30 – EUR 17 – EUR 4) for 0.50 MWh or EUR 18/MWh
Same steam from 95% efficient boiler would cost EUR 32/MWh

SOURCE: McKinsey Resource-Productive Operations service line

Getting started: Lean tools for resource productivity

To improve quality and root out waste, companies can use a battery of tools to support lean methods. In the classic product focus, the tools track losses and process flaws that affect a product's quality and cost. From the perspective of resource productivity, the tools chart resource losses across the production process. In the pages that follow, we introduce three useful diagnostic tools that lay the foundation for a lean approach to resource productivity.

- Utility and resource contract baseline—understand current financial situation
- Value stream mapping—discover process steps that add value
- Resource-loss framework and waste walk—identify process inefficiencies.

Utility and resource contract baseline

This tool uses a series of matrices to determine how much a company spends on the resources it consumes. The principle is powerful and straightforward. In the context of energy, for example, energy is lost at internal makeup (that is, transforming and transporting) and at each stage of a production process. The overall energy costs, however, remain constant.

The utility matrices calculate baseline energy costs from three perspectives that map to value chain logic: purchasing, makeup and transportation, and consuming and selling (Exhibit 13):

- **Variable purchase cost** constitutes the costs for energy at the front of the system. To arrive at variable costs, companies should analyze utility contracts and identify fixed costs. Energy contracts often stipulate fixed fees and include penalties for the breach of various provisions. Deducting the fixed costs from the total energy spending shows the variable energy costs that a company can influence through improved resource productivity.
- **Makeup and transportation cost** constitutes the costs of transforming and transporting a purchased utility, such as coal, into a

consumed utility, such as steam. By linking the purchased costs of a utility to the costs of transforming it, this matrix shows the fully loaded cost of utilities created for the production process.

- **Consumed and sales cost** is a matrix that allocates the fully loaded utility cost to each piece of equipment or external customer that consumes it, revealing resource costs at a granular level.

Exhibit 13

EXHIBIT 13

Different baselines are linked with tables called utility matrices

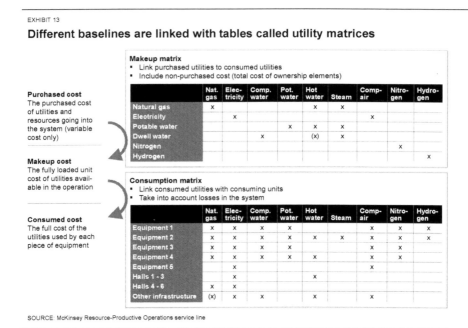

Purchased cost
The purchased cost of utilities and resources going into the system (variable cost only)

Makeup cost
The fully loaded unit cost of utilities available in the operation

Consumed cost
The full cost of the utilities used by each piece of equipment

Makeup matrix
- Link purchased utilities to consumed utilities
- Include non-purchased cost (total cost of ownership elements)

	Nat. gas	Elec-tricity	Comp. water	Pot. water	Hot water	Steam	Comp-air	Nitro-gen	Hydro-gen
Natural gas	x				x	x			
Electricity		x					x		
Potable water				x	x	x			
Dwell water		x			(x)	x			
Nitrogen								x	
Hydrogen									x

Consumption matrix
- Link consumed utilities with consuming units
- Take into account losses in the system

	Nat. gas	Elec-tricity	Comp. water	Pot. water	Hot water	Steam	Comp-air	Nitro-gen	Hydro-gen
Equipment 1	x	x	x	x			x	x	x
Equipment 2	x	x	x	x	x	x	x	x	x
Equipment 3	x	x	x	x			x	x	
Equipment 4	x	x	x	x	x		x	x	
Equipment 5		x					x		
Halls 1 - 3		x			x				
Halls 4 - 6	x	x							
Other infrastructure	(x)	x	x		x		x		

SOURCE: McKinsey Resource-Productive Operations service line

For each baseline, the total cost remains the same. For example, in a cogeneration process, which creates electricity and steam from natural gas, the cost of the gas used in the cogeneration should equal the value of both the electricity and the steam produced (at their opportunity cost). Because the main objective of the cogeneration is to produce steam, the generated electricity is considered a by-product. The generated electricity is valued at the variable purchasing price of electricity using opportunity price logic. This means that the only variable left is the price of steam, which is set by subtracting the value of the electricity generated from the purchased fuel cost. This implies that the price of the steam is lowered as electricity tends to be more valuable than fuel and the conversion from fuel to electricity is close to 100 percent efficient in non-condensing stages of a cogeneration unit (Exhibit 13).

Energy from alternative sources such as windmills and the by-products of other processes requires a few additional calculations as they should be included at opportunity price in the purchased baseline.

Building a raw materials baseline should only include the variable costs of raw materials, waste handling, and consumables associated with the sale of products and by-products. At this stage, it is valuable to calculate a preliminary estimate of the value at stake from yield losses. To estimate that value, managers need to determine how much material the process would consume for a given amount of output had the process operated at 100 percent stoichiometric efficiency. Subtracting the actual performance from the potential, including by-product sales and consumables consumption, provides the yield loss: the total opportunity for improvement.

Factoring in the free available energy

Certain processes will generate energy yet have no apparent variable costs—for example, steam recovery from the burning of sulfur to produce sulfuring acid, coke-oven gas recovered from the steel coking process, or on-site windmills. To account for these energy sources, we add them to the utility and resource contract baseline as opportunity costs, represented as revenue losses or additional costs that would have been incurred had these sources been purchased. In the paper and pulp industry, for example, net energy costs are often only 5 percent or less of total expenses. Most of the needed energy is generated from a by-product (black liquor) through combustion in recovery boilers and associated steam turbines. Factoring in recovered energy as an opportunity cost would increase energy to 10 to 15 percent of total production costs.

Resource value stream mapping

In its classic product application, value stream mapping follows a product through the factory and identifies steps that can be streamlined and sources of waste that can be eliminated. To improve resource productivity, value stream mapping follows the flow of resources from the point of generation to each process step at which it is consumed. The mapping process also analyzes the factory layout by adding machine locations to the energy-flow map.

Value stream mapping takes place at a high level. It charts the flow of material and energy though different process steps and links the utility matrix to raw material consumption. Using mass balances for each process step, the value chain can be visualized as a resource Sankey diagram (Exhibit 14)—cost losses are included before the bottleneck process steps and full revenue losses are included. In addition, value stream mapping can be performed at a more granular level and serve as a technical map of the process under investigation (Exhibit 15).

Exhibit 14

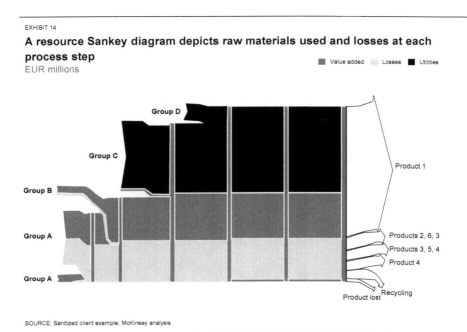

EXHIBIT 14

A resource Sankey diagram depicts raw materials used and losses at each process step
EUR millions

Value added ▨ Losses ░ Utilities ■

Group D

Group C

Group B

Group A

Group A

Product 1

Products 2, 6, 3
Products 3, 5, 4
Product 4

Product lost Recycling

SOURCE: Sanitized client example; McKinsey analysis

Value stream mapping identifies specific improvement opportunities. These opportunities surface through a diligent focus on conversion points that affect utility parameters (such as pressure, temperature, flow, electrical consumption, and control method) and variances in utility parameters (including heat in exhaust or sewage).

Exhibit 15

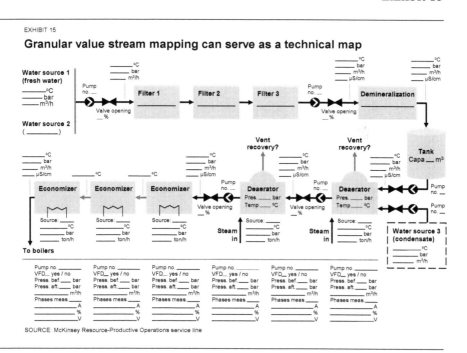

EXHIBIT 15

Granular value stream mapping can serve as a technical map

SOURCE: McKinsey Resource-Productive Operations service line

Value stream mapping can reveal key sources of waste, including the following:

- Overproduction such as vented steam
- Transport issues including heat losses, redundant networks, and networks that are unnecessarily long
- Suboptimized systems including oversized pumps and fans working against a constant throttle
- Overprocessing such as unnecessarily high pressure in compressed air networks.

Energy and mass balances need to be calculated when building a utility matrix and value stream map. We include them here in an example of an energy-flow diagram (Exhibit 16).

Exhibit 16

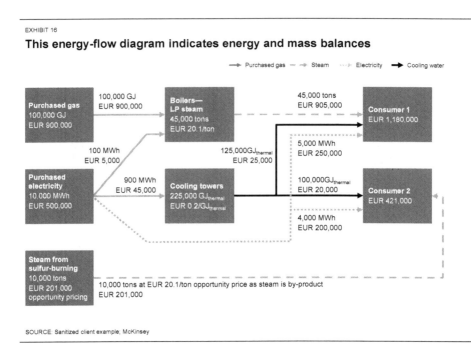

EXHIBIT 16

This energy-flow diagram indicates energy and mass balances

SOURCE: Sanitized client example; McKinsey

Waste walk and resource-loss framework

The purpose of a waste walk, also known as a Gemba walk, is to observe the production process to see where waste and loss might be occurring (Exhibit 17). A waste walk can yield 20 or 30 issues for further analysis and testing. Waste walks are a powerful tool that managers can use regularly to identify potential improvement areas and demonstrate their commitment to the shop floor. For energy change agents, the waste walk provides a first impression of the situation and an opportunity to generate an initial list of improvement ideas.

When conducting a waste walk, managers should walk along the flow of major utilities, observing major processes and product lines. They should be sure to not only look, but listen to find equipment issues including air and water leaks, improperly maintained equipment, and idling. They can take a heat camera to find insulation issues, measure temperatures, and get a sense of where heat is being lost.

Exhibit 17

EXHIBIT 17

Waste walks help companies identify waste and resource losses

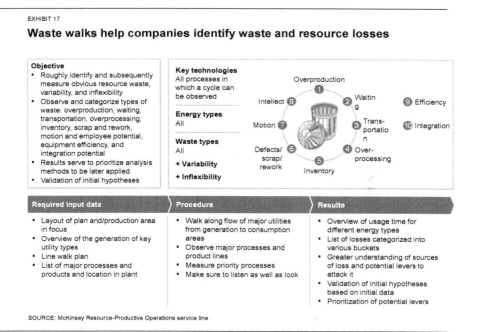

Objective
- Roughly identify and subsequently measure obvious resource waste, variability, and inflexibility
- Observe and categorize types of waste: overproduction, waiting, transportation, overprocessing, inventory, scrap and rework, motion and employee potential, equipment efficiency, and integration potential
- Results serve to prioritize analysis methods to be later applied
- Validation of initial hypotheses

Key technologies
All processes in which a cycle can be observed

Energy types
All

Waste types
All
+ Variability
+ Inflexibility

Overproduction 1
Waiting 2
Transportation 3
Overprocessing 4
Inventory 5
Defects/scrap/rework 6
Motion 7
Intellect 8
Efficiency 9
Integration 10

Required input data	Procedure	Results
• Layout of plan and/production area in focus • Overview of the generation of key utility types • Line walk plan • List of major processes and products and location in plant	• Walk along flow of major utilities from generation to consumption areas • Observe major processes and product lines • Measure priority processes • Make sure to listen as well as look	• Overview of usage time for different energy types • List of losses categorized into various buckets • Greater understanding of sources of loss and potential levers to attack it • Validation of initial hypotheses based on initial data • Prioritization of potential levers

SOURCE: McKinsey Resource-Productive Operations service line

Managers should also talk to operators in order to understand the issues they see and probe how important resource productivity is in their view, as a test of the key performance indicators in use. A waste walk should also survey the control room, where managers can track how energy moves through the process and identify losses such as inefficient equipment and open bypasses in the system. In the control room, managers can examine temperature flows to spot opportunities for energy integration and assess how the company measures the performance of its production processes. They can control for excessive electricity use by managing valve positions and for process stability by examining past data trends.

***

Because resource-productivity improvements can involve a great deal of leading-edge technology, it can be tempting to define resource productivity as primarily a technical challenge. However, such an approach often misses the bigger picture of where the greatest resource-productivity opportunities lie. Applying lean principles to resource productivity reveals that bigger picture. Because many companies already use many lean principles, adding resource productivity to the mix can give a strong impetus to improvement efforts by leveraging well-known approaches understood by a broad base of people in the company.

CHAPTER 4

THINK LIMITS

*M*any organizations approach resource productivity by making incremental improvements to their current operating state. A major difference in our approach is a focus on theoretical limits. We consider the absolute ideal state, meaning a production process with no mechanical or chemical losses and perfect energy utilization, and establish that as a baseline objective. Such a goal is clearly unattainable in the real world, but it results in a more comprehensive way of identifying and analyzing losses. Fully aligned with lean thinking, the concept of the theoretical limit generates buy-in from mid-level technical experts and line workers alike. Most important, it leads to greater improvement in yield and energy use.*

The theoretical limit

When many organizations think about resource productivity, they typically look at their current operations and search for levers to improve the process. That's an understandable impulse, but it represents only a partial solution that limits their thinking and leads to incremental solutions—at best.

Instead, organizations that are truly interested in resource productivity should "think limits." That is, they should begin by mapping out the theoretical limit of the current process to determine how it would look under ideal conditions, without any losses from mechanical issues, nonstandard processes, flawed raw materials, or other sources. This becomes the baseline: the theoretical limit of what's possible. Next, the organization tries to identify all losses in the gap between their current operations and this theoretical limit and to understand what's driving those losses (Exhibit 18). Finally, it develops solutions to reduce or eliminate those losses.

The theoretical-limit concept applies to both yield and energy, and it represents a far more comprehensive approach that allows the company to set ambitious goals and stretch targets. It is similar to the overall equipment effectiveness (OEE) concept, which in turn is based on lean principles, so many organizations will already be familiar with the underlying rationale. As with those concepts, the focus is on identifying losses and waste—that is, any steps that do not introduce value—and then working to eliminate them.

Exhibit 18

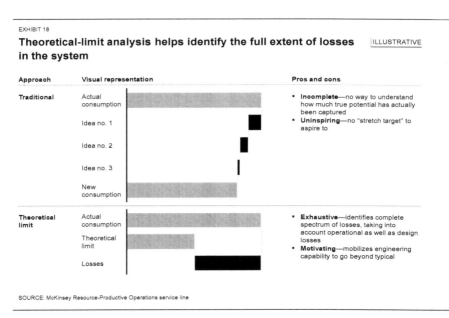

EXHIBIT 18

Theoretical-limit analysis helps identify the full extent of losses in the system   ILLUSTRATIVE

Approach	Visual representation		Pros and cons
Traditional	Actual consumption		• **Incomplete**—no way to understand how much true potential has actually been captured
	Idea no. 1		• **Uninspiring**—no "stretch target" to aspire to
	Idea no. 2		
	Idea no. 3		
	New consumption		
Theoretical limit	Actual consumption		• **Exhaustive**—identifies complete spectrum of losses, taking into account operational as well as design losses
	Theoretical limit		• **Motivating**—mobilizes engineering capability to go beyond typical
	Losses		

SOURCE: McKinsey Resource-Productive Operations service line

A good analogy from process industries is the maintenance concept of "tool time": the value-added period when employees are actually on a job site, working with tools in hand. All other time is effectively wasted. In some cases, that waste is unavoidable, though still addressable—for example, the "incidental" loss when employees are traveling to the equipment they are to maintain or are in training (travel time can, for example, be addressed when providing bikes or cars to employees or creating local spare parts stores—this will require capex in most cases though). Yet, other categories of time are actually wasted—such as time when they arrive on-site and have to wait for equipment to be shut down or for work permits that could have been prepared in advance. The objective is to make value-added time, or tool time, the largest possible proportion of a maintenance worker's day, by identifying and eliminating all possible sources of loss.

Advantages of the theoretical limit

The theoretical limit is truly "theoretical" in that it is based on the laws of physics and chemistry. In most cases, it can't actually be achieved in the real world. Yet it is a way to look at all resources and all potential sources of loss. As such, it constitutes a breakthrough. With conventional thinking on energy and yield, many companies consider their equipment design to be the limiting factor. Moreover, they bundle losses due to operations—for example, a worker who routinely sets a temperature incorrectly—into the broader category of "equipment losses." (To illustrate, the classic Sankey diagram is a powerful visualization tool, but it does not have any way of indicating operational losses, which can be significant.)

Defining the theoretical limit requires different methodologies depending on the situation. For example, the theoretical limit for the yield of a chemical process can be calculated at a basic level using stoichiometry, and more refined versions can take chemical equilibria and kinetics into consideration. For an endothermic reaction, it can be calculated as the amount of energy required for the reaction according to thermodynamic principles.

In some processes, the theoretical limit cannot be mathematically calculated, but it can be determined through simulations or experiments. In rolling mills, the company can run the equipment both with and without product. In fermentation processes, the organization can look at the best possible outcome of each component step and add those together.

Starting with the theoretical limit offers several clear advantages described below.

Exhaustive

First, it's exhaustive—leaving no place for losses to hide. For example, in a batch reactor, engineers starting with the classic approach—looking for improvement Levers—did not find substantial improvement potential. By applying the theoretical limit, however, the company found that it could not explain 15 percent of the energy consumption. This led to further investigation, and ultimately the managers determined that the energy in question was being lost through the control loop, as the temperature control was overshooting, creating quick-succession cycles of heating and cooling to keep the temperature constant. The company would not have uncovered these losses without applying the theoretical-limit-method concept. As one manager said, "You squeezed us like lemons."

Flexible

Second, the theoretical-limit concept is flexible. Rather than requiring specific levers for specific situations, it is universally applicable across virtually all industries and processes, including, for example, for chemistry electrolysis, batch, continuous, and semicontinuous processes. Consider a company that manufactures industrial chemicals that was able to apply the theoretical-limit methodology across its three principal business lines—paints, coatings, and specialty chemicals— even though all three have completely different production processes. After undergoing a 12-week training program in theoretical-limit analyses, a central team was able to travel to several of the company's production facilities and implement the new way of thinking.

Motivating

Third, the theoretical-limit concept is motivating. Instead of a set of edicts that headquarters issues to production facilities, it gives engineers the kind of challenge they respond to—a calculation of what's possible, a chance to analyze the losses that are preventing them from getting there, and time to deepen their understanding of the equipment. Because they are central to the analysis, and are needed to develop the solution, engineers and other stakeholders are motivated to buy into the theoretical-limit process.

Impactful

Last—and most important—the theoretical limit is impactful. In general, it results in savings that are two or even three times larger than those identified using other methodologies.

For example, the management team at one steel company brought in a consultant team to analyze its operations using conventional methodology—starting with current operations and looking for improvement levers. Through that process, the company identified an energy savings of 6 percent, mainly at downstream operations. Right after that, we contacted the company about the McKinsey approach. The executive team told us that they had just undergone a similar cost-savings initiative, but that we were welcome to come in and see if we could find anything else. Using our theoretical-limit approach, we identified an additional 8 percent savings in energy—more than doubling the initial savings, and all with measures that had a payback period of less than two years.

One reason that the methodology is so impactful is that the ideas stem from many of the engineers and line workers themselves—similar to lean. Thus, there's a greater interest and enthusiasm for actually seeing such ideas implemented. Take the example of a North American steel manufacturer, where previous energy studies led to 108 improvement ideas. That sounds impressive, until you learn that of that total, only 8 were actually implemented (Exhibit 19). Why so few? Primarily because these 108 ideas came from outside the organization. They were handed down like a set of mandates to engineers and mid-level managers who had designed the process and had long been using it.

Exhibit 19

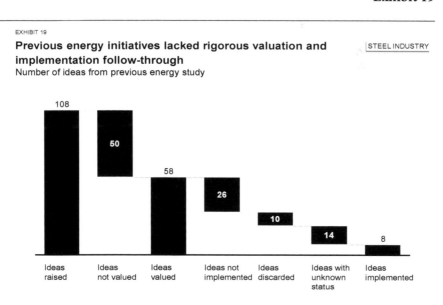

EXHIBIT 19

Previous energy initiatives lacked rigorous valuation and implementation follow-through
Number of ideas from previous energy study

STEEL INDUSTRY

SOURCE: Sanitized client example; McKinsey analysis

By contrast, the theoretical-limit concept helps engineers and mid-level managers diagnose the problem themselves and gives them a framework for designing and implementing solutions. At the same North American steel manufacturer, an initial top-down self-assessment generated just 3.3 percent in savings. During a brainstorming session with mid-level engineers, that potential savings increased to more than 7 percent. And a series of line walks with frontline employees pushed the total savings above 10 percent. Of that last category, the majority of ideas from the line walks did not require any capital expenditure, and those that did require such expenditure had a payback period of two years or less.

This is common—ideas that come from the top tend to involve significant investment, often with little input from the people actually operating the machinery. By contrast, a bottom-up approach tends to generate a lot of small, low-cost ideas that collectively add up to significant savings.

The logic of the theoretical limit

Theoretical-limit analysis is a powerful tool, yet it follows a fairly straightforward logic. A plant starts by determining its actual energy consumption. (Again, the principle applies to energy, yield, and even to resources like materials, utilities, and water; in this discussion, though, we'll focus on an example related to energy.) It then looks at operational losses, or those related to process design. Removing all operational losses should lead to the organization's best demonstrated performance—the lowest actual energy consumption for a particular day over a given period of time, typically a year. (It is important to note that because the performance on individual days sometimes stems from outlying events, such as extreme weather, some organizations prefer to use "best repeated performance." This is the average of their lowest sequence of consecutive days— typically three, five, or seven—in a given year.)

Next, the organization looks at design losses. This refers to losses associated with the way the equipment was previously designed.

Identifying and mitigating all operational and design losses yields the theoretical limit for a given process or facility.

These elements are typically shown on a visualization tool called a "loss bridge." A loss bridge identifies and categorizes all categories of loss. It answers the questions: Where am I today? Where should I be? How far can I go? In essence, loss bridges are a way to visualize the gap between current performance and the theoretical limit. In addition, they provide a means of breaking down that gap into its constituent components. They can be used to analyze a central parameter (such as yield, energy, throughput, or environmental waste), a process (like chemical reaction, steel reheating, or axel turning), or even a piece of equipment (such as a pump, heat exchanger, or compressor) (Exhibit 20).

Exhibit 20

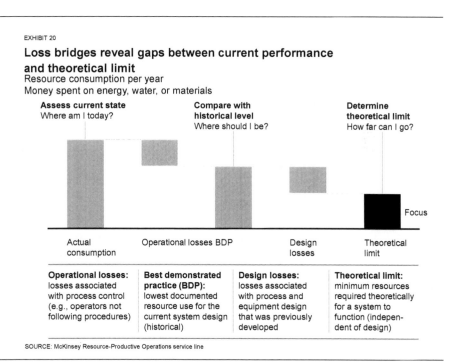

EXHIBIT 20

Loss bridges reveal gaps between current performance and theoretical limit
Resource consumption per year
Money spent on energy, water, or materials

Assess current state
Where am I today?

Compare with historical level
Where should I be?

Determine theoretical limit
How far can I go?

Focus

Actual consumption	Operational losses BDP	Design losses	Theoretical limit

Operational losses: losses associated with process control (e.g., operators not following procedures)	Best demonstrated practice (BDP): lowest documented resource use for the current system design (historical)	Design losses: losses associated with process and equipment design that was previously developed	Theoretical limit: minimum resources required theoretically for a system to function (independent of design)

SOURCE: McKinsey Resource-Productive Operations service line

Both broad categories of losses—operational and design—apply in all theoretical-limit analyses. The components within those categories will differ depending on the application. However, the description that follows summarizes operational losses for yield.

Operational losses

Operational losses are associated with process control—the way that equipment is run, for example, or the way that a manufacturing step takes place in the plant. They follow the typical OEE framework (Exhibit 21).

- **Availability:** Availability losses are defined as the energy consumed when the line is down, such as air-conditioning or the minimal power supplied to machinery in its idle state. Theoretically, if you were to run a factory 24 hours a day, with no breakdowns or stops for maintenance, you would have no availability losses—all energy consumed would be adding value and resulting in product.
- **Product mix:** Different products require different parameters in production, such as temperatures, durations, and energy required. The product mix is defined by external factors—customer demand, profitability of specific items—along with internal considerations. (For example, if a plant does not have enough raw material to produce a batch of material A, it will switch the line to material B, but that may be a less efficient use of the equipment.) All of these switches between products in the mix invariably lead to losses. (Again, the theoretical consideration here is that if a plant were to make only one product, the process could be optimized for that product, and product mix losses would be minimized or, ideally, reduced to zero.)
- **Load:** Plant equipment has a throughput level at which it is operating at maximum efficiency; however, for various reasons, it cannot always remain consistently at that load factor. Any deviations from that point lead to losses. (We discuss this

concept in greater detail later in this chapter; see the section "Load curves.")

Exhibit 21

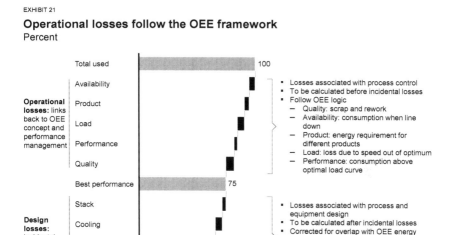

EXHIBIT 21

Operational losses follow the OEE framework
Percent

SOURCE: McKinsey Resource-Productive Operations service line

- **Performance:** Performance losses are a broader category that includes operator errors (such as using incorrect equipment settings or deviating from standard practices). This category also includes losses stemming from problems with equipment, such as belts that are not lubricated or other maintenance issues that impact performance. These are identified using the load curve.

- **Quality:** If a factory makes a product that doesn't meet prescribed quality requirements, the product has to be either scrapped or reworked. That's inevitable, but the flawed batch leads to losses in both energy and yield, which must be accounted for.

A case in point: Addressing performance losses in an iron and steel company

A large iron and steel enterprise in China recently underwent an operational transformation effort. Several of the organization's practices were outdated, and a great deal of the company's equipment was being improperly used. As a result, instrument devices were damaged and the corresponding workshops and procedures were operated inefficiently.

The organization identified several opportunities to use waste heat for power generation. More notably, it realized that improper equipment management was leading to many unexpected shutdowns. To address this, the company developed an improved set of operations strategies and reestablished design parameters for its equipment. Within one month, the power generation through waste heat from several production components increased as much as 25 percent, resulting in a reduction of RMB 10 per ton of iron produced. A subsequent phase of waste-heat power generation is expected to yield at least an additional RMB 4 to 6 per ton reduction of iron cost, equivalent to a net income of RMB 28 million annually and total potential savings of RMB 45 million.

A case in point: Reducing electricity consumption in the electrolytic aluminum industry

Electrolytic aluminum involves conventional, high-energy-consuming processes; each ton of electrolytic aluminum consumes 13,000 to 14,000 kilowatt-hours of electricity, and annual electrolytic aluminum production capacity reaches about 23 million tons; meanwhile, electricity cost accounts for about half of the production cost of electrolytic aluminum.

To address this, a large aluminum group used the theoretical-limit concept facilities. It analyzed all production steps in the process, determined to develop a pilot test at one of it's the lowest theoretical energy needed for that step, and sought improvements to get there. As a result, the company was able to reduce its energy consumption by 300 kilowatt-hours per ton of aluminum.

Best demonstrated performance

Once you account for all operational losses, you're at the point of "best demonstrated performance."

Another way to think about this is that it's akin to a "brownfield" situation: the best performance you can possibly wring out of the existing equipment and operators. By contrast, the next category, design losses, are those associated with the equipment itself, such as the stack, cooling system, and radiation, and the standard operating procedures in place for that equipment (for example, setting the superheat at the center 10 degrees higher than what's required by the process and safety margins).

Mitigating design losses is akin to a "greenfield" situation. If you replaced specific components—such as a new stack that includes a heat exchanger—you could reduce design losses and get closer to the theoretical limit.

Design losses

By definition, reducing design losses almost always entails some level of capital investment—such as upgrading or replacing the stack, cooling system, heat exchanger, or production equipment. For understandable reasons, many organizations think they can only improve their resource productivity only by taking such steps. The thinking is that they're currently wringing the best possible performance out of the equipment they have.

Based on our experience, this is frequently not the case. We generally suggest focusing on operational losses first, for several reasons. First, addressing operational losses generally requires little or no capital expenditure, and these solutions tend to be "quick wins" that come from the bottom up. That is, they come through ideas generated by line workers and mid-level technical managers—who can quickly see the gains that their ideas generate. A focus on operational losses often shows plant employees and managers the many types of loss that are "hiding in plain sight." In the aggregate, these ideas to reduce operational losses may add up to more than total design losses. Moreover, they help employees develop a more comprehensive understanding of the equipment, how it works, and how to maximize its potential. They also make employees invested in any performance-enhancing initiatives.

Theoretical-limit tools

As in other areas of resource productivity, we have a set of tools that we use to make theoretical-limit analyses and calculations. Each is discussed in detail below.

Load curves

Load curves are a key performance indicator for energy consumption. They show energy consumption per unit as a function of throughput. To use a load curve, the organization plots historical data over a given period of time and then connects the data points with a fit function through the points. The line shows that for higher throughputs, a facility will have lower specific—or per-unit—energy consumption (Exhibit 22).

Exhibit 22

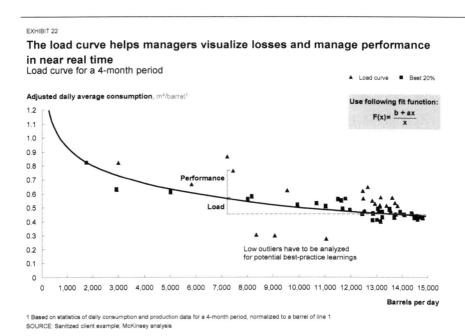

EXHIBIT 22

The load curve helps managers visualize losses and manage performance in near real time
Load curve for a 4-month period

▲ Load curve   ■ Best 20%

Adjusted daily average consumption, m³/barrel[1]

Use following fit function:
$$F(x) = \frac{b + ax}{x}$$

Performance

Load

Low outliers have to be analyzed for potential best-practice learnings

Barrels per day

1 Based on statistics of daily consumption and production data for a 4-month period, normalized to a barrel of line 1
SOURCE: Sanitized client example; McKinsey analysis

There is another factor to consider, however. Energy consumption generally gets broken down into two components: fixed and variable. The fixed component is the baseline consumption, which is independent of how much finished product a facility generates. It comes from simply turning on the machinery and not running any raw material through it. The variable component is the energy consumption that is associated with how much product you are generating. More product requires greater energy usage.

Some plant managers make the mistake of assuming that their energy usage is either 100 percent fixed (which is not true) or 100 percent variable (also not true). Instead, it's usually somewhere in the middle, and this has implications when it comes to energy-saving measures. For example, in some cases, reducing throughput in an attempt to save energy will reduce total usage, but the specific energy consumption—or the amount of energy for a unit of finished goods—will actually increase. Why? Because the drop in variable costs is not enough to offset the fixed component. Because of this effect, managers need to use load curves to manage their energy consumption and correct for changes in production speed.

The load curve also establishes a predicted level of energy consumption for a given throughput, based on historical performance. How is this used? A plant manager can look at throughput levels for a given day and determine what the energy consumption should have been—it should fall directly on the line. If the actual performance is below the line, that reflects an unanticipated savings. If it's above the line, that reflects a performance loss.

Among operational losses, as discussed previously, the load curve shows both load losses (as indicated by the shape of the line) and performance losses (shown by how far above the line a particular day's specific energy consumption sits).

The load curve is useful in that it helps managers visualize losses and manage performance in near real time. For example, in the daily production meeting, a manager can discuss the prior day's performance with line employees and, for sizable deviations, look into potential root causes. Was it an especially warm day in summer or a cold day in winter? Did the line workers deviate in some way from standard operating procedures?

Shutdown analysis

Shutdown analysis is a tool that organizations apply when they have large availability losses—that is, high energy usage when the equipment is not producing value-added product. This can be a significant source of loss, particularly for plants that only operate one shift during weekdays. That schedule means the equipment is sitting idle the remaining 16 hours every weekday, plus another 48 hours on the weekends. Longer and more predictable shutdowns—like those required for substantial maintenance or repairs—offer still larger potential gains, in that they allow the organization to go "deep" and turn off the greatest amount of equipment. However, plants can also capture and eliminate losses during shorter periods like lunch breaks.

In all categories, the manager must understand energy consumption patterns and have a systematic approach for shutdowns that factors in both length and predictability and sets clear priorities for which equipment—and in which order. Managers must also have a means in place to avoid any problems that may limit shutdowns. Often, the biggest problem is a lack of cost awareness on the part of employees, who may feel that a shutdown for a short period "is too time-consuming" or requires them to keep track of too many things. Often, these obstacles related to mind-set can only be identified through a line walk during an actual shutdown. In this scenario, managers can watch the process in action and ask detailed questions. In these cases, standard operating procedures can help. In addition, an automated system that controls shutdowns may generate enough savings to justify the capital expenditure.

Start-up also matters. By analyzing the various energy loads among components on an assembly line, an organization can determine the most efficient way to power everything up after a stop—for example, turning on high-consumption equipment last. (These are essentially shutdowns in reverse, but the same loss principles apply.)

Demand curve and cost curve analysis

Demand and cost curves are another valuable tool in theoretical-limit analysis (Exhibit 23). Together, they give a visual indication of energy costs as a function of capacity for multiple pieces of equipment. For example, the exhibit shows the demand and cost curves for compressed air at a given facility. The chart on the left (the demand curve) shows how much compressed air the facility requires and for what percentage of the time at specific levels. The facility shown requires peak volume (175 m³ per hour) only about 5 percent of the time, and a lower amount (110 m³ per hour) far more frequently, about 50 percent of the time.

The chart on the right (the cost curve) shows the capacity and cost to operate the facility's seven air compressors. The shorter bars, compressors 1 and 2, cost less to operate, and the taller bars, compressors 6 and 7, cost more.

If an organization understands its demand for the utility in question—if, for instance, the manager knows that 200 cubic meters per hour is the maximum demand load for a specific process, as indicated by the dotted vertical line in the exhibit—it can use the cost curve to determine which compressors it should run to achieve that load (starting with those on the left, which have a lower total cost of operation [TCO]) and which to turn off (those on the right, which have a higher TCO).

In practice, a manager can overlay the two curves and get a clear indication of which compressors he or she needs to run, and for what percentage of time, in order to meet demand.

Exhibit 23

EXHIBIT 23

Demand and cost curves are key to theoretical-limit analysis

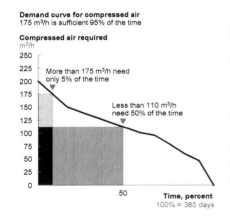

Demand curve for compressed air
175 m³/h is sufficient 95% of the time

Compressed air required
m³/h

More than 175 m³/h need only 5% of the time

Less than 110 m³/h need 50% of the time

Time, percent
100% = 365 days

Cost curve for compressed air ■ Current usage

Cost
EUR/m³

Maximum load of 200 m³/h

Compressor 1, Compressor 2, Compressor 3, Compressor 4, Compressor 5, Compressor 6, Compressor 7

Compressor capacity
m³/h

Comparing utilities demand over time with the utilities cost curve makes it possible to reduce total cost of ownership (e.g., shutting down compressors)
3 compressors are sufficient to generate 175 m³/h; 7 compressors in operation

SOURCE: Sanitized client example; McKinsey analysis

Network analysis

Network analysis is yet another tool for helping companies define the theoretical limit and improve their energy consumption performance. It allows a facility to better match supply and demand for a given utility—such as steam, cooling water, or compressed air—by showing its distribution through the facility's network. For example, the steam provision at different pressures throughout the network might involve pressure-reducing valves, which effectively waste that utility. Instead, back-pressure turbines are available that could make valuable electricity from that pressure reduction.

To determine how those entities can possibly be better aligned, the organization must draw a network map. The map gives a visual indication of the interconnection points—with associated parameters such as temperature, pressure, flow, and valve openings; key equipment such as pumps and turbines; and the logic used to connect them. The resulting map shows where the manager can make improvements to reduce losses in the delivery of that utility. It also indicates points where a facility can potentially shut off or start up production components more efficiently at different production regimes (Exhibit 24).

Also worth noting is that the aforementioned cost curve links to the network map. If a plant has two steam boilers and each one feeds a turbine independently, both boilers and both turbines must always be on line. By contrast, if either boiler could provide steam for each turbine independently, the facility could potentially operate them more efficiently. The network map shows these restrictions, thereby highlighting the opportunities.

Resource-lifecycle analysis

The principle of resource-lifecycle analysis is fairly simple: it is a type of mass and energy balance that exclusively looks at a single resource. The tool is typically applied to steam, because the energy and mass can be tracked and recycled fairly easily (though it can also be used for pressure via a liquid medium, like cooling water, thereby mapping the pressure and flow energy lost along the path the medium follows). Consider steam

EXHIBIT 24

The network map depicts interconnection points
Example steam network[1]

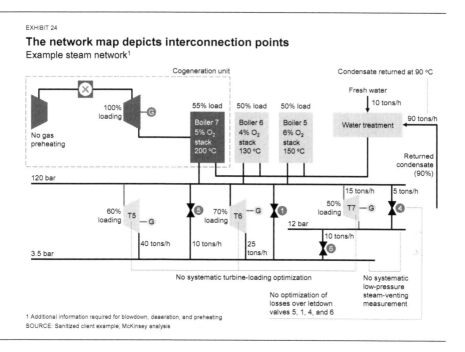

1 Additional information required for blowdown, deaeration, and preheating
SOURCE: Sanitized client example; McKinsey analysis

condensate (Exhibit 25). The exhibit shows the resource-lifecycle analysis for a given facility. Starting from the left, it shows steam (and condensate) at various pressures. The size of the block shows the flow volume in tons per hour.

As the exhibit indicates, the total volume leaving the powerhouse is 1,500 tons per hour, yet only 1,000 tons per hour are returned to the powerhouse. The remaining 500 tons per hour is lost. Some of that is consumed by the production process (an unavoidable category of loss), yet another component goes up the vent—potentially because of overproduction. Still, other losses leak out as sewage, yet the end result is undeniable: the facility must "make up" 500 tons of water per hour of production. The electrical and chemical cost to produce that makeup water is significant—up to EUR 2 to 3 per m³—and the heat contained in the condensate is also not reused, meaning a value loss of another EUR 2 to 3 per m³.

Exhibit 25

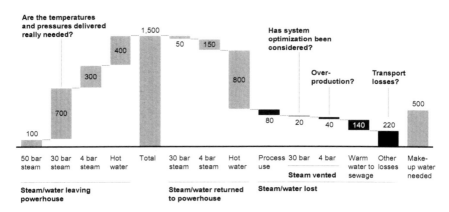

EXHIBIT 25

Resource-lifecycle analysis looks at a single resource
Steam and condensate, tons/h

SOURCE: Sanitized client example; McKinsey analysis

By showing such losses explicitly in an end-to-end balance, the resource-lifecycle analysis allows a production manager to identify and analyze them and potentially take steps to reduce them.

Temperature mapping ("quick pinch") analysis

The final theoretical-limit tool is temperature mapping analysis (also known as "quick pinch"). This process shows where a facility might reduce losses in the way that heat is transferred into and out of a production process. The goal is to identify losses—that is, places where the facility is unnecessarily heating up or cooling down materials. These losses can be due to overproduction, overprocessing, heat losses due to radiation, or the use of unnecessarily expensive utilities (for example, chilled water, which requires energy, instead of cooling water, which is often readily available and costs less). Temperature mapping also identifies potential integration opportunities, or points out where heat may be used to warm up a cold component in the process, and vice versa.

EXHIBIT 26

Temperature mapping reveals heat and cooling integration potential   ILLUSTRATIVE

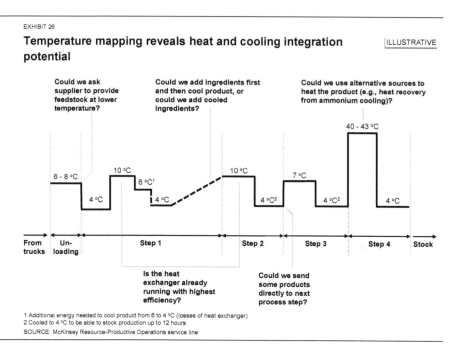

Could we ask supplier to provide feedstock at lower temperature?

Could we add ingredients first and then cool product, or could we add cooled ingredients?

Could we use alternative sources to heat the product (e.g., heat recovery from ammonium cooling)?

40 - 43 °C

6 - 8 °C

10 °C

6 °C[1]

10 °C

7 °C

4 °C

4 °C

4 °C[2]

4 °C[2]

4 °C

From trucks

Un-loading

Step 1

Step 2

Step 3

Step 4

Stock

Is the heat exchanger already running with highest efficiency?

Could we send some products directly to next process step?

1 Additional energy needed to cool product from 6 to 4 °C (losses of heat exchanger)
2 Cooled to 4 °C to be able to stock production up to 12 hours
SOURCE: McKinsey Resource-Productive Operations service line

To assemble a temperature map, you must track the temperature of a medium (often the product, its raw materials, or water) as it moves through the factory. Imagine dropping a tiny thermometer into the production stream and recording temperatures at each stage of production. The map also shows places where the medium is actively heated or cooled, along with the utility used (Exhibit 26). All changes in temperature represent areas to investigate. Are those changes truly necessary?

Is there a way to limit the temperature swings required for a specific step in the process? (Existing heat integration is shown on the map by a dotted line.)

A more advanced version of this is the "full pinch," which employs a basic vector logic but tracks both a hot curve and a cold curve. The hot curve plots temperature and heat added by each active source (such as steam), and the cold curve plots temperature, along with the heat removed by each cooling source. The process gets repeated for all product in the plant—all active heating and cooling efforts—and aggregated on a single

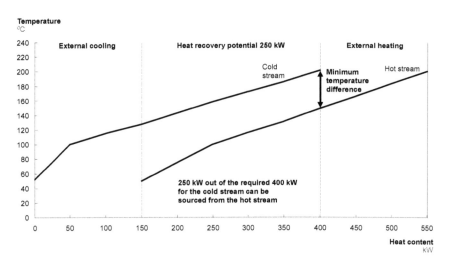

EXHIBIT 27

Full pinch analysis tracks both hot and cold curves

Temperature
°C

External cooling   Heat recovery potential 250 kW   External heating

Cold stream   Minimum temperature difference   Hot stream

250 kW out of the required 400 kW
for the cold stream can be
sourced from the hot stream

Heat content
kW

SOURCE: McKinsey Resource-Productive Operations service line

map. Because the line for each medium is a basic vector, where the start and end points reflect the temperature difference, they can be combined mathematically, to show all heating and cooling efforts for the facility on two simple lines (Exhibit 27). In this way, the full pinch analysis identifies the theoretical limit of heat-integration opportunities—or the sum of all potential ways to reduce wasted heat or cooling. Then, a manager can see if there are opportunities to "pinch"—or bring the two lines closer together, as if pinching them with his or her fingers.

It's worth noting that this process can become extremely complex; indeed, some third-party providers specialize in full pinch analysis. While that may be worth pursuing in some situations—as with refineries—the quick pinch is fast, easy, and sufficient for most organizations.

Do's and don'ts of theoretical-limit calculations

Finally, while the theoretical limit is a powerful tool for developing resource-productive operations, there are some clear guidelines regarding its use. Specifically:

Do ...

- Deeply understand the factors involved and how they produce or consume energy or product yield.
- Be as creative as possible in how to calculate the limit. (For example, if a theoretical calculation is not available, as is the case with fermentation and some other processes, use past best performance and break the process into constituent steps or even set up an experiment.)
- In situations where you don't have metered data, formulate hypotheses to determine where losses might be occurring.
- Be consistent in methodologies and outputs, particularly when calculating limits for several facilities, components, or business units.

Don't ...

- Consider limits and losses as end products; rather, they are tools intended to help employees generate ideas.
- Insist on perfectly rigorous calculations. In many cases, estimates and hypotheses are sufficient to capture sizable losses.
- Exclude production components without having a clear understanding of their "appetite" for energy or how they lead to yield loss.

CHAPTER 5

THINK PROFIT PER HOUR

*I*n many organizations, resource-productivity responsibilities are divided between functions and units, an approach that ends up leaving money on the table. Production managers, for example, are striving for improvements in output while energy managers focus on reducing energy consumption. The efforts rarely come together. To break down silos and maximize resource productivity, companies are turning to a powerful new metric: profit per hour.

Wanted: A new perspective on profit

Businesses have always focused on profit. However, they typically calculate it on a monthly or quarterly basis. Profit per hour, on the other hand, is a real-time operational metric that can unite disparate functions and perspectives within an organization through the lingua franca of profit. Though easy as concept, it only became usable recently through advances in data collection and accessibility, that is, big data in production environments.

Consider the experience of a large site at a specialty chemical company. The organization was proud of its resource-productivity accomplishments. Besides a strong track record of improvements dating back to the 1960s, the site's average yield performance was very high by industry standards, and multiple studies of its energy efficiency found limited potential for further gains. However, a deeper look leveraging profit per hour found that the site was missing significant opportunities: the financial equivalent of the payroll of all 800 employees.

A closer look at profit per hour

Profit per hour factors energy and resource costs into the total profit equation of production processes, including product mix, at any point in time. It is more robust and comprehensive than metrics such as cost per megawatt-hour or kilogram of product produced. These measures don't capture the complex trade-offs among energy consumption, yield, throughput, and waste. Increasing reactor temperatures, for example, consumes more energy but can also boost yield. Similarly, more excess material in a reactor can reduce yield. But it can also increase throughput and decrease cycle time.

Profit per hour builds on a logic similar to overall equipment effectiveness to create a holistic measure that delineates the economic impact of these trade-offs. By focusing on all elements that generate profit at any given time, the new metric breaks down silos by rallying the organization around the common language of money.

Exhibit 28

EXHIBIT 28

Profit per hour calculates gross profit for a given time period   ☐ Typical focus of work
Overall optimization formula

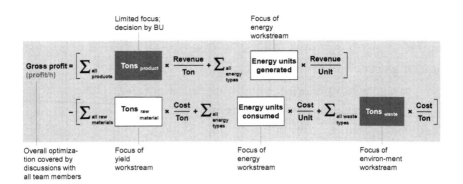

- Team typically focuses on yield as well as on consumed and generated energy and environment
- The team needs to prioritize how to balance efforts between workstreams
- While the final optimization is on profit, ideas are being generated in each workstream
- Price landscape as well as customer demand are typically taken as given

SOURCE: McKinsey Resource-Productive Operations service line

The experience of a large European oil company is a prime example. The organization produces diesel fuel, gasoline, and several by-products, such as kerosene. Diesel and gasoline are the most valuable, and the company's equipment is designed to produce them. As a result, the company's production allocation process focused heavily on these products. However, the business had the capacity to produce highly profitable by-products—but these opportunities never came to light at the enterprise level.

The production department realized that the company had the capacity to produce more by-products without increasing energy consumption. But no one asked them to produce it. Senior management and sales also understood the potential of by-products but never put it in business plans because they didn't know about the available capacity.

Profit-per-hour analysis brought the opportunity to light and made it an agenda item with a clear profit opportunity. Production now informs sales of its capacity to produce specific by-products. With that knowledge, sales can include by-products in its business plan that management factors into the company's strategy. Increasing by-products has added more than EUR 1 million to the company coffers annually. The effort was by no means a onetime gain. Cross-functional teams regularly meet to surface profitable new opportunities.

Spotlight on the profit-per-hour equation

At the highest level, profit per hour calculates an operation's gross profit for any given period of time by subtracting overall costs, including energy and resources, from revenue (Exhibit 28). The earnings side of the equation includes revenue per ton of product and revenue for each unit of energy generated. The cost side captures raw material expenses as well as energy costs associated with steam, electricity, compressed air, water, and emission controls.

Moving from lean to green

Profit per hour takes its cue from lean manufacturing. In lean's classic application, companies focus on throughput (Exhibit 29). The goal is to minimize fixed costs, such as labor and depreciation, by improving variables including labor productivity and performance management. In the past, companies considered variable costs of energy, environment, and yield as less important because labor and machinery were the largest expense and they believed they had already largely optimized yield. However, as raw materials and energy become more scarce and costly, regular monitoring of their related costs now plays a much bigger role in financial success.

Focusing solely on throughput, however, misses the opportunities inherent in the bigger picture. Energy consumption, environmental waste, yield, and throughput are inextricably linked and need to be optimized in tandem. By applying the concept of theoretical limits to these system elements, companies can make the optimal tradeoff decisions by understanding the financial impact of each choice (Exhibit 30). Understanding the financial impact of trade-offs can make organizations more agile, which is critical during downturns, when costs are more important than outputs. Profit per hour is a powerful metric that flexes an organization's ability to be agile.

Exhibit 29

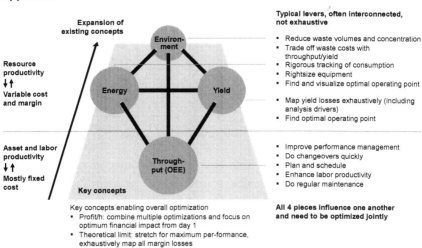

EXHIBIT 29

Resource-productive manufacturing complements the standard lean approach

Expansion of existing concepts

Resource productivity
↓↑
Variable cost and margin

Environ-ment

Energy — Yield

Asset and labor productivity
↓↑
Mostly fixed cost

Through-put (OEE)

Key concepts

Typical levers, often interconnected, not exhaustive

- Reduce waste volumes and concentration
- Trade off waste costs with throughput/yield
- Rigorous tracking of consumption
- Rightsize equipment
- Find and visualize optimal operating point

- Map yield losses exhaustively (including analysis drivers)
- Find optimal operating point

- Improve performance management
- Do changeovers quickly
- Plan and schedule
- Enhance labor productivity
- Do regular maintenance

Key concepts enabling overall optimization
- Profit/h: combine multiple optimizations and focus on optimum financial impact from day 1
- Theoretical limit: stretch for maximum per-formance, exhaustively map all margin losses

All 4 pieces influence one another and need to be optimized jointly

SOURCE: McKinsey Resource-Productive Operations service line

These examples from the chemical industry illustrate the range of interdependencies:

- Reducing throughput can reduce energy consumption but at the expense of less product produced.
- Improving yield can increase energy consumption. Chemical reactions, for example, can be increased by raising temperatures and applying better stirring techniques to the raw materials. Both of these tactics, however, consume more energy.
- Increasing yield can reduce throughput. For example, the yield from a given reaction grows as the reaction time increases. However, a longer reactor time reduces capacity for other, more profitable reactions and products.
- Improving yield reduces waste.
- Reducing energy consumption can cut down on CO_2 emissions.
- Increasing throughput increases waste. Even at maximum efficiency, waste increases as throughput grows.

Exhibit 30

EXHIBIT 30

Assessing interdependencies helps companies prioritize resource initiatives

In the past, optimization efforts typically focused on only one element at a time ...

... but with resource-productive operations, companies need to understand trade-offs when determining where to focus their efforts

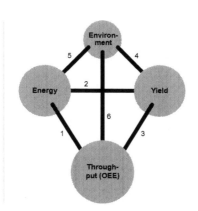

Examples of interdependencies

1 Lower energy consumption can be achieved with lower throughput

2 Increasing yield can increase energy consumption

3 Increasing yield can reduce throughput

4 Yield increase also reduces waste to be disposed

5 Improving energy consumption can reduce CO_2 emissions

6 Increasing throughput can increase waste

Making the connections: The power of 1 percent

When seeking improvements in resource productivity, many companies stop at the raw materials. However, understanding the optimal trade-offs inherent in energy, environmental waste, yield, and throughput can add considerable gains. Just a 1 percent improvement taking these factors into account can improve resource productivity, even in cases of highly efficient raw material use. Moreover, for large companies, 1 percent is anything but trivial. Identifying its sources lays the groundwork for more aggressive targets.

Consider the example of a specialty chemical company that was focusing on its use of ethylene, its largest-volume raw material. It was paying much less attention to other drivers such as oxygen loss in the reactions and steam loss during heating. Adding these and other drivers into the equation revealed potential opportunities that rivaled any improvements in ethylene use (Exhibit 31).

Exhibit 31

EXHIBIT 31

A specialty chemical company identified the 1 percent opportunity

Overall assumptions	Cost-based analysis	Sales-based analysis
• No separate shutdown for catalyst changes; opportunity to change catalyst once a year • Cost and savings are distributed evenly over the lifetime of catalyst to calculate yearly cost/savings	• To produce same amount of product, less ethylene is used	• More product 1 produced using same amount of ethylene

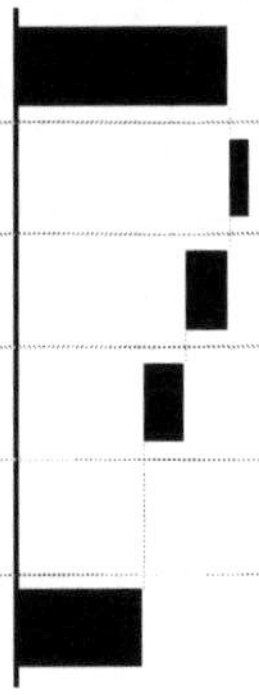

Description of effect

Ethylene savings/ additional revenues	• Raw materials not consumed in side reaction to make CO_2	• Additional product 1 sales
O_2 savings	• Raw materials not consumed in side reaction to make CO_2	• Difference in O_2 consumption between side reaction and desired reaction
Steam losses	• Strongly exothermic side reaction to CO_2 generates heat • Efficiency of heat exchangers at 62%	• Difference in heat generation between side reaction and desired reaction
Additional catalyst cost	• Cost of additional catalyst change	• Same as cost based
Other	• Placeholder for potential additional cost, (e.g., CO_2 certificates); all negligibly small at present	• Same as cost based
Total		

Taking into account margins of product 1 captive use would further increase potential

SOURCE: Sanitized client example; McKinsey analysis

To see this larger picture of resource productivity, the specialty chemical company used the value-at-stake tool. The tool helps create quick calculations of each improvement's value and generates a prioritized list of opportunities for further analysis. From a cost perspective, the organization saw significant upside if it could increase the yield of ethylene reactions, which would reduce the amount of raw material needed. Equally important, if the plant could cut down its oxygen and steam losses, it could replace catalysts less frequently. Both of those scenarios have a significant impact on sales. If the company could reduce the amount of ethylene and oxygen it uses in its primary products, those resources could be diverted to other products without increasing resource costs.

The company looked at these relationships through the lens of profit drivers such as shifts in demand and price. A decline in market demand, for example, could lead to shutdowns, which affect throughput, which ultimately reduces profit.

After assessing the relative importance of these factors, the organization found that interconnections between throughput and yield were most important, followed by yield and energy (Exhibit 32). The impact of energy stemmed from exothermic side reactions that reduced yields but increased the amount of energy that could be recovered. In turn, that reduced the energy that the company needed to purchase.

The sales perspective

To prioritize products in a business plan, it is natural for companies to look at profitability. Costs are a major component of the profit equation, and many manufacturers often calculate them in terms of costs per kilogram of product produced. However, looking at costs solely in terms of volume can be very misleading. Assume that a company is evaluating two products and finds that one is three times more profitable than the other when measured in terms of cost per unit produced. The business would logically focus on the more profitable product.

But what if the more profitable product takes five times as long to produce? The business could be destroying margin by downplaying a product that is actually more profitable than the cost per unit metric indicates. Profit per hour brings these opportunities into stark relief.

EXHIBIT 32

Companies must prioritize interactions with the greatest impact

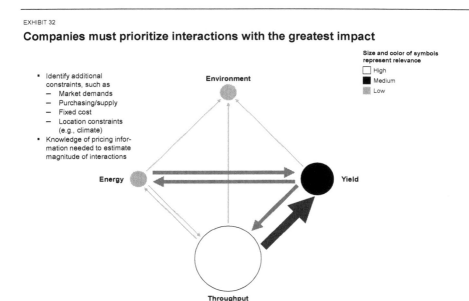

Size and color of symbols
represent relevance
☐ High
■ Medium
▨ Low

- Identify additional
  constraints, such as
  — Market demands
  — Purchasing/supply
  — Fixed cost
  — Location constraints
    (e.g., climate)
- Knowledge of pricing infor-
  mation needed to estimate
  magnitude of interactions

Environment

Energy

Yield

Throughput

SOURCE: McKinsey Resource-Productive Operations service line

A major European life sciences company is a prime example. The enterprise was focusing on two major products that were highly profitable in terms of gross profit per unit. But when the company assessed its product mix in terms of profit per hour, a very different picture emerged. The company discovered that its major products were actually less profitable per hour—and thus over time—than several other products that had not been the organization's focus before.

By using profit per hour, companies can also eliminate the need to produce product at a higher quality than wanted by customers. For example, an integrated chemical company wanted to ensure that it always adhered to the minimum water level industry standard of 500 parts per minute (ppm) in its polyvinyl chloride. It set the water level at 300 ppm to make sure that it would never exceed 400 ppm and risk going over the 500 ppm standard. By taking a profit-per-hour perspective, it became clear to production managers how producing polyvinyl chloride with water levels beyond what customers expected was reducing profit. They spearheaded efforts to exert better control over the production process and were able to consistently manufacture with water levels at 400 ppm.

The procurement perspective

Purchasing is almost always driven by price, and the procurement organization is often rewarded for reducing costs. Although price is certainly important, effective purchase decisions should also take these three variables into account:

- **Availability:** A company may be able to procure materials very inexpensively from countries such as the Republic of the Congo. However, these countries suffer from political instabilities that can cause long delivery delays.
- **Quality:** Similarly, businesses can purchase materials from companies in countries such as Russia, where delivery is much more reliable. However, quality can fluctuate and fail to meet specifications.
- **Value:** Materials that meet delivery and specification requirements may not be optimal for the company's operations. Low-quality iron ore may be very inexpensive, for example. However, its high sulfur and phosphate content can make it difficult to produce high-quality steel, which drives up costs.

Value-in-use analysis balances these variables by optimizing them for the company's production processes. Consider the example of a metals company. The organization produces zinc and precious metals. It operates four plants and can procure raw material from more than 20 different sources. To optimize the value in use of raw materials, the metals company experimented with different feed mixes and ultimately found a balance of variables that increased its earnings before interest, taxes, depreciation, and amortization (EBITDA) by 44 percent (Exhibit 33).

The production perspective

In Chapter 3 ("Think lean") we introduced the concept of value stream mapping. In its classic manufacturing use, value stream mapping follows a product through the factory and pinpoints steps that can be streamlined

EXHIBIT 33

A mining company optimized feed mix to discover the optimal value in use

Main changes in feed mix, thousand tons

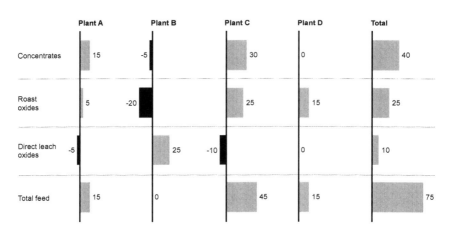

SOURCE: Sanitized client example; McKinsey analysis

and sources of waste that can be eliminated. In its application to resource productivity, value stream mapping follows the flow of resources from the point of generation through each process step at which they are consumed. The goal is to identify process points where resource productivity can be enhanced.

To increase profit per hour, companies start with a value stream map and then probe the drivers beneath each process point to identify the most powerful improvement opportunities. Three primary tools help managers see the deeper opportunities: the resource Sankey diagram—cost losses are included before the bottleneck process steps and full revenue losses are included (see Chapter 3), the yield-driver tree, and advanced analytics.

In the specialty chemical company example we cited at the beginning of this chapter, value stream mapping identified key production-process points where yield could be improved such as reactors, absorbers, and distillation. Using the yield-driver tree, the organization then found the

A case in point: A smelting enterprise improves raw material efficiency

A world-class, state-owned aluminum smelting enterprise in China recently improved its energy-efficiency management during production. Subsequently, it wanted to improve its energy efficiency by examining the purchase of upstream raw materials. The company laid out a pilot with a self-owned power plant of an aluminum-oxide enterprise. It looked at the purchase of coal used to power the boiler. Instead of simply buying for the highest possible heat value over the longest period of time, the company determined that some of the coal heating value was not adding value to the process. Therefore, it began purchasing a blend of different coal types, with low, medium, and high heat value, and determined how much energy it would need to add in order to pulverize and blend the coal so that it would meet the requirements for stable boiler operation. In sum, the company was able to generate the same amount of steam at a lower price, saving RMB 2.9 per ton of finished product.

Two years later, a Chinese state-owned specialty steel manufacturer wanted to apply the same concept of value-based purchasing to ore. However, ore blending is more difficult because ore is a bulk commodity with daily price fluctuations and companies must deal with the link between inventory and spot goods. Additionally, ensuring the stable operation of blast furnaces is extremely important during iron smelting, requiring consistent blending processes.

In response to these challenges, the company looked at both purchasing and production. In regard to purchasing, it perfected its evaluation system to make strategic purchases. In regard to production, the team established the right model for blending ore. The entire value-based molten-iron purchasing model generated a savings of RMB 90 to 120 per ton of molten iron in a pilot test. Applying that model to all blast furnaces in the group could lead to annualized spending reductions of 3 to 4 percent on iron ore.

EXHIBIT 34

A specialty chemical company identified resource-productivity value drivers

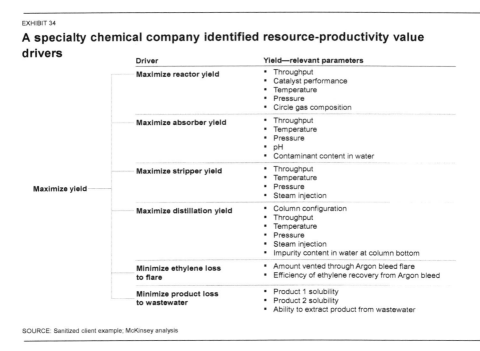

Driver	Yield—relevant parameters
Maximize reactor yield	• Throughput • Catalyst performance • Temperature • Pressure • Circle gas composition
Maximize absorber yield	• Throughput • Temperature • Pressure • pH • Contaminant content in water
Maximize stripper yield	• Throughput • Temperature • Pressure • Steam injection
Maximize distillation yield	• Column configuration • Throughput • Temperature • Pressure • Steam injection • Impurity content in water at column bottom
Minimize ethylene loss to flare	• Amount vented through Argon bleed flare • Efficiency of ethylene recovery from Argon bleed
Minimize product loss to wastewater	• Product 1 solubility • Product 2 solubility • Ability to extract product from wastewater

Maximize yield

SOURCE: Sanitized client example; McKinsey analysis

primary sources of improvement at each of those points. For example, temperature and pressure were significant because increasing either could boost yield. Similarly, reactor throughput could have a significant impact because increasing it could reduce the yield (Exhibit 34).

The integrated perspective

Bringing departments together to optimize resource productivity, production, procurement, and sales can deliver powerful results. To achieve those results, all managers involved need a complete view of the opportunities in their production systems. They must also be prepared to contend with a number of complexities:

- **Interlinked flows:** It is often difficult to intervene at discrete process steps in refineries and chemical plants. These production processes are continuous, and product moves through the system in pipes.

- **Interlinked sites**: Organizations often have several sites or factories producing the same or similar products for the same customers. This poses production allocation questions and means that companies must consider factors such as labor arbitrage and the value of proximity to customers.
- **Make-or-buy decisions**: Many companies face major trade-offs between options such as buying power from the grid or investing in a power plant.
- **Multiple possible outputs**: Businesses must determine what percentage of their capacity should be devoted to which products.
- **Cost and price variability**: Product and raw material prices can be volatile, and most companies struggle to assess the impact of that volatility on a frequent basis.
- **Multiple product inputs**: As discussed, purchase decisions in regard to raw materials must balance cost with quality.
- **Alternative manufacturing routings**: Operations can be configured in multiple ways. A chemical company, for example, could use three tanks for a product that requires three reactions or use two tanks in parallel flowing to a third tank for a product that requires only two reactions.
- **Transfer pricing**: Even at its best, transfer pricing is a somewhat arbitrary exercise because it isn't based on actual value in the market. As a result, transfer pricing often leads to bias in decisions by implying a level of profitability between different parts of the organization that may not be the case.

Companies face significant organizational barriers when tackling the complexity of their systems. Often driven by pay-per-performance incentives, individual units and managers focus on improving their domains alone and not overall enterprise performance. In addition, data are often trapped in different systems with no single platform that integrates them. Cost data for utilities and raw materials are often in one system, revenue information in another, and production system data in yet another. When data are so disparate, companies can't assess their operations with any

Exhibit 35

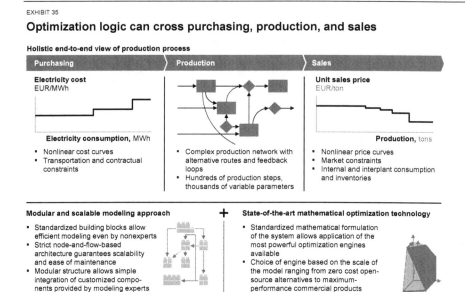

EXHIBIT 35

Optimization logic can cross purchasing, production, and sales

Holistic end-to-end view of production process

| Purchasing | Production | Sales |

Electricity cost
EUR/MWh

Unit sales price
EUR/ton

Electricity consumption, MWh

Production, tons

- Nonlinear cost curves
- Transportation and contractual constraints

- Complex production network with alternative routes and feedback loops
- Hundreds of production steps, thousands of variable parameters

- Nonlinear price curves
- Market constraints
- Internal and interplant consumption and inventories

Modular and scalable modeling approach **+** **State-of-the-art mathematical optimization technology**

- Standardized building blocks allow efficient modeling even by nonexperts
- Strict node-and-flow-based architecture guarantees scalability and ease of maintenance
- Modular structure allows simple integration of customized components provided by modeling experts

- Standardized mathematical formulation of the system allows application of the most powerful optimization engines available
- Choice of engine based on the scale of the model ranging from zero cost open-source alternatives to maximum-performance commercial products

SOURCE: McKinsey analysis

ease or frequency. Additionally, the problem often becomes so complex that no one individual can make sense of it.

To manage this complexity and find the right operating point, companies generally need to create models that can apply state-of-the-art optimization logic across purchasing, production, and sales (Exhibit 35). Models should be structured so that they are modular and scalable, enabling companies to update and expand them.

In addition, models should be built for sustainability. That means they should be easy to maintain and rely on a familiar format, like Microsoft Excel, for the interface, though more powerful languages will be required for the core. Model output should be a set of reports that are functional and concise so that they align with company sales and operations planning (S&OP) processes (Exhibit 36).

For example, the specialty chemical company we have discussed used profit per hour to overcome these barriers and tackle the

EXHIBIT 36

A focus on usability helps companies manage complexity

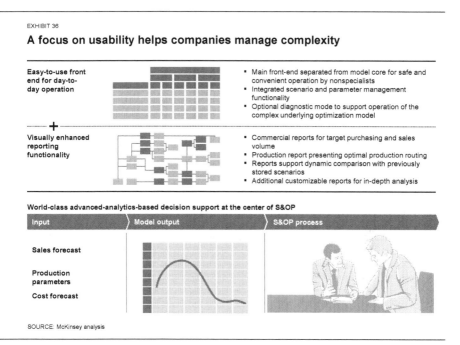

Easy-to-use front end for day-to-day operation	• Main front-end separated from model core for safe and convenient operation by nonspecialists • Integrated scenario and parameter management functionality • Optional diagnostic mode to support operation of the complex underlying optimization model
Visually enhanced reporting functionality	• Commercial reports for target purchasing and sales volume • Production report presenting optimal production routing • Reports support dynamic comparison with previously stored scenarios • Additional customizable reports for in-depth analysis

World-class advanced-analytics-based decision support at the center of S&OP

Input	Model output	S&OP process
Sales forecast		
Production parameters		
Cost forecast		

SOURCE: McKinsey analysis

complex challenges in optimizing its operations. The organization has multiple plants with a variety of bottlenecks, including producing by-products from waste. For example, when the capacity of the central waste processing unit reaches its limit, it can slow all production volumes, including by-products made from the waste. To optimize the system, a cross-functional team modeled the entire operation and the profitability of potential trade-offs, as previously described. The results were significant: the company increased its EBITDA by more than 50 percent.

Beyond 1 percent: Advanced analytics

The interdependencies between drivers and their potential parameters, such as raw material quality, can amount to millions of possible combinations. Companies need to discover those that will have the greatest impact on profit per hour.

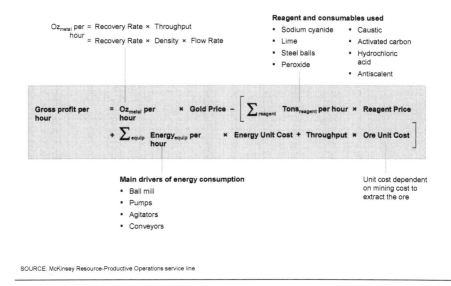

EXHIBIT 37

A precious metals mining company calculated profit per hour

SOURCE: McKinsey Resource-Productive Operations service line

Neural networks, a form of artificial intelligence, identify the most potent combinations. Simulating how the human brain works, neural networks assimilate data, rules, and hypotheses and use algorithms to learn from assumptions applied to enormous data sets.

A precious metals mining company based in EMEA used neural networks to reveal drivers of 5 to 10 percent increases in profit per hour. The organization began by creating its profit-per-hour equation (Exhibit 37). In precious metals, the primary drivers of revenue and profit include the recovery rate (how much metal the leaching process extracts from the ore) and throughput (which is driven by density and flow rates). The leaching process uses a number of reagents (including sodium cyanide), as well as lime and steel balls. The main drivers of energy consumption are the ball mill, pumps, agitators, and conveyors.

In any leaching process, there is a trade-off between yield and throughput. In the case of precious metals mining, focusing solely on those trade-offs could reduce profit when ore prices rise or precious metal prices fall beyond a certain point. To develop a more robust approach, the company analyzed other drivers and their parameters that could potentially increase the incremental production of precious metal.

The mining company found that its optimum yield came from a fairly narrow range of ore grade—between 0.7 and 0.9 g per ton. When the company looked at grade more granularly, however, it found no discernable patterns (Exhibit 38).

To understand what was at play, the mining company turned to neural networks to isolate specific days and events where the yield should have been higher (Exhibit 39). The exhibit shows those points of deviation that theoretically should have been smaller. The gray line shows actual yield. The green line suggests what the yield should have been. The arrows indicate points where the deviation was significant and further investigation was required. To determine what drivers and parameters caused the variation, the mining company conducted a root cause analysis.

Exhibit 38

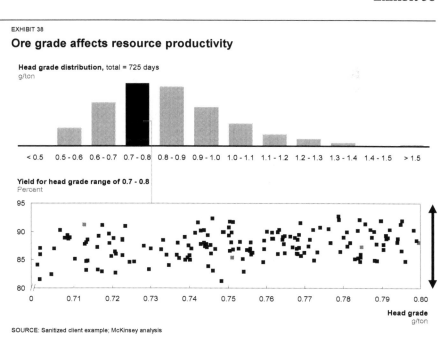

EXHIBIT 38

Ore grade affects resource productivity

Head grade distribution, total = 725 days
g/ton

| < 0.5 | 0.5 - 0.6 | 0.6 - 0.7 | 0.7 - 0.8 | 0.8 - 0.9 | 0.9 - 1.0 | 1.0 - 1.1 | 1.1 - 1.2 | 1.2 - 1.3 | 1.3 - 1.4 | 1.4 - 1.5 | > 1.5 |

Yield for head grade range of 0.7 - 0.8
Percent

Head grade
g/ton

SOURCE: Sanitized client example; McKinsey analysis

Exhibit 39

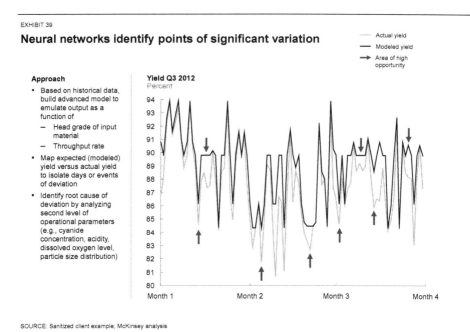

EXHIBIT 39

Neural networks identify points of significant variation

— Actual yield
— Modeled yield
➡ Area of high opportunity

Approach
- Based on historical data, build advanced model to emulate output as a function of
  - Head grade of input material
  - Throughput rate
- Map expected (modeled) yield versus actual yield to isolate days or events of deviation
- Identify root cause of deviation by analyzing second level of operational parameters (e.g., cyanide concentration, acidity, dissolved oxygen level, particle size distribution)

Yield Q3 2012
Percent

SOURCE: Sanitized client example; McKinsey analysis

They focused on second-order parameters including cyanide concentration, acidity, and level of dissolved oxygen.

The results were illuminating. Increasing the oxygen concentration improved yield to the same degree as optimizing the grade of raw material—each contributing a 3 percent improvement (Exhibit 40). As a result, the company could increase its precious metals production by 8 percent in three months. If these results were rolled out across the mining industry, it would boost industry profit by EUR 30 billion to EUR 40 billion.

Spotlight on the money in water

Unless located in regions where water is scarce, business leaders often see water as an inexpensive resource. Managing water use is an exercise in documenting its foot-print—how much the company uses and where—as part of its sustainability reporting. The prevailing attitude only makes

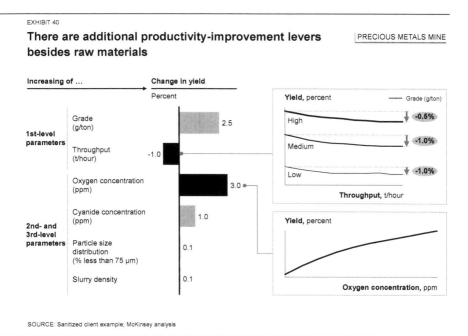

EXHIBIT 40

There are additional productivity-improvement levers besides raw materials

PRECIOUS METALS MINE

SOURCE: Sanitized client example; McKinsey analysis

sense if water costs were solely an issue of their tariff. When looking at water as a carrier that includes what a company puts into and can extract from it, the improvement opportunities jump dramatically—as much as 100 times the actual water cost (Exhibit 41).

For example, water contains energy used to heat and cool. If that energy isn't recaptured, it is simply lost. Companies also add chemicals to water to treat it and meet pollution mitigation requirements. In addition, if excess water is heated, these costs are lost. If excess chemicals are used to treat products, these often go down the drain.

Consider the experience of a paper and pulp company. It analyzed its costs of water, including carrier costs, and found that it was wasting some EUR 20 million every year (Exhibit 42). The tariff costs of its water were only EUR 200,000 per year. But when the company factored in wastewater, chemicals, heat, and product losses (in this case, fiber that could be used in paper), the number jumped 100-fold.

Exhibit 41

EXHIBIT 41

The carrier concept helps organizations assess water-related costs

- What matters for companies is what you put into water and what you get out of it
- Water itself often has negligible costs
- However, all the energy, chemicals, and product put into the water may constitute a significant portion of a company's operating expenditure
- Meanwhile, all the heat, energy, and nutrients that leave the plant in the wastewater may be profitable opportunities missed

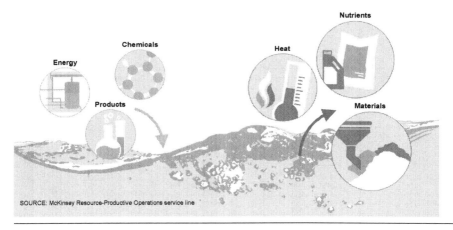

SOURCE: McKinsey Resource-Productive Operations service line

How harnessing big data can help

Companies have huge amounts of data, and the volume is growing faster than most organizations can process. The use of embedded machine-to-machine sensors is mounting at the rate of 30 percent annually, and these sensors are currently installed in everything from cars, roads, and buildings to appliances and medical devices. Intercompany and consumer activity generates trillions of data points. The list could go on.

Despite the plethora of data, companies struggle to connect the dots between the data they have and the systems needed to analyze and interpret them. The challenges range from failing to capture data in the first place to not using them in decisions when they are available (Exhibit 43). Being able to connect the dots with data is no longer something that is "nice to have." Increasingly, businesses need an analytics capability to remain competitive and address high-stakes challenges.

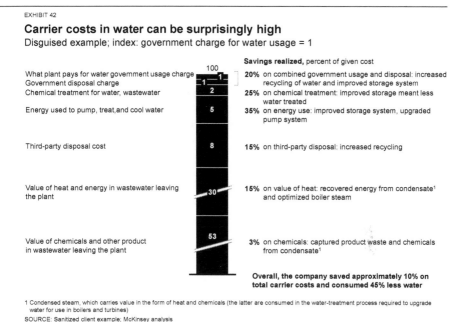

EXHIBIT 42

Carrier costs in water can be surprisingly high
Disguised example; index: government charge for water usage = 1

Savings realized, percent of given cost

	Index	Savings
What plant pays for water government usage charge	100 / 1	**20%** on combined government usage and disposal: increased
Government disposal charge	1	recycling of water and improved storage system
Chemical treatment for water, wastewater	2	**25%** on chemical treatment: improved storage meant less water treated
Energy used to pump, treat, and cool water	5	**35%** on energy use: improved storage system, upgraded pump system
Third-party disposal cost	8	**15%** on third-party disposal: increased recycling
Value of heat and energy in wastewater leaving the plant	30	**15%** on value of heat: recovered energy from condensate[1] and optimized boiler steam
Value of chemicals and other product in wastewater leaving the plant	53	**3%** on chemicals: captured product waste and chemicals from condensate[1]

Overall, the company saved approximately 10% on total carrier costs and consumed 45% less water

1 Condensed steam, which carries value in the form of heat and chemicals (the latter are consumed in the water-treatment process required to upgrade water for use in boilers and turbines)
SOURCE: Sanitized client example; McKinsey analysis

A large biopharmaceutical company, for example, was having production issues with its vaccines. Yields were low, which put a damper on profits. But variability in product quality was of greater concern. The company didn't understand the causes of that variation, and regulators were voicing concerns.

The data that the company needed in order to address the issues, however, were essentially in a black box. They were housed in multiple IT systems; furthermore, a great deal of data were handwritten. As a result, there was no practical way for the company to harness the data it had to discover the solutions it needed to implement. To resolve the issue, the organization extracted data from its multiple sources and put them into an analytics platform. Then, the company was able to build predictive models to identify the optimum process-parameter settings. Using those predictive models, the biopharma company increased its vaccine yield by more than 50 percent and stabilized process variation to the satisfaction of regulators.

Exhibit 43

EXHIBIT 43

Companies face multiple barriers to harnessing big data

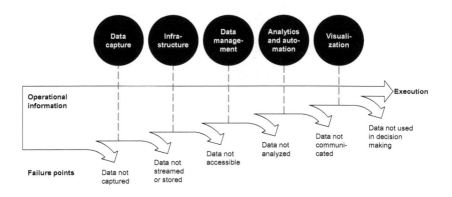

SOURCE: McKinsey Resource-Productive Operations service line

***

As raw materials become scarce and more expensive, corralling resource-productivity efforts can play a significant role in a company's financial success. Unfortunately, most improvement efforts occur in silos and rarely combine into a coordinated effort based on a holistic enterprise view. Profit per hour provides that view through a lingua franca financial measure that defines the economic impact of a myriad of choices at any given moment in time. With that measure, sales, production, and procurement have a new lens for evaluating their decisions and working cross-functionally to discover new opportunities.

Chapter 6

THINK HOLISTIC

*R*eaching resource-productivity goals requires a thoroughgoing transformation, which is no small endeavor. Managers must set meaningful and achievable goals and persuade an often reluctant organization to embrace and pursue them. Even if businesses garner the buy-in of
their employees, they must also equip them with skills and deploy new management systems to ensure that goals are met. Based on our research and experience, we have found that successful change requires three components—
technical systems, management infrastructure, and mind-sets, capabilities,
and behaviors—which must fit together like interlocking gears.

Change program shortfalls

The failure rate of change programs is notoriously high—as many as two-
thirds fail to take off, stall in midflight, or otherwise fall short of expectations.[23] Resource-productivity programs are no exception. Highly capable
companies have missed sustainability targets and have had to revise
them—to the consternation of nongovernmental organizations, investors,
and the public.

Why companies fail to achieve resource-productive transformations
is one of the most heavily researched and debated issues in management.
Much of the discussion, however, focuses on cultural issues. McKinsey
spent three years probing the issue more deeply and holistically. In an
exhaustive study, we surveyed some 600,000 managers, 7,000 senior
executives, and engaged leading academics to review and pressure test

---

23   Kotter, John: "Leading change: Why transformation efforts fail," *Harvard Business Review,*
     January 2007, as cited in the *McKinsey Quarterly Transformational Change Survey,* 2010.

our findings. The research revealed that successful organizational transformations are propelled by three core elements that drive each other like interlocking gears (Exhibit 44):

- **Technical systems:** The assets and equipment that a company owns and the processes that people perform with those assets to create value.
- **Management infrastructure:** The formal management structures, processes, and systems that companies use to manage people and technical systems.
- **Mind-sets, capabilities, and behaviors:** The attitudes that drive behavior individually and collectively.

As with gears, each relies on the others to operate at an effective speed. The relationship is analogous to driving a car. The engine is the technical system. If it is not designed well or is inadequately maintained,

Exhibit 44

EXHIBIT 44

Three interlocking gears can drive resource productivity

Formal structures, processes, and systems through which the technical system is managed to deliver business objectives

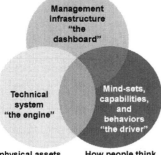

How physical assets and resources are configured and optimized to create value and minimize losses

How people think, feel, and conduct themselves in the workplace, individually and collectively

SOURCE: McKinsey

the car performs poorly. The dashboard is the management system. If it is flawed, the driver may have no idea how fast he or she is going or whether the car has enough fuel. Drivers are the mind-set and behavior part of the equation. If they are ignorant or disrespectful of the rules of the road, the other elements won't prevent an accident.

Many resource-productivity programs are constrained because companies neglect one of the gears. For example, many organizations invest heavily in technologies to improve technical systems without deploying management processes driven by a comprehensive view of resource loss. By the same token, businesses are often unaware of mind-sets that stand in the way of their progress. For instance, many people believe that compressed air is cheap when, in fact, it is one of the most expensive energy utilities.

In the sections that follow, we provide a road map for successful change based on our research and experience. We offer insights, best practices, and examples of how the three elements of organizational transformation are being applied successfully to resource productivity. We flank the discussion with two components that underlie progress and turn the gears: leadership and the building of capabilities.

The leadership dimension

A large North American steel manufacturer seemed to have all the elements in place for improving resource productivity. Executives were aware that their company spent some USD 300 million on energy and were dedicated to reducing those costs. The company also had highly skilled engineers who were diligently looking for opportunities to improve energy efficiency. The company's leaders had established corporate-level key performance indicators (KPIs) including energy cost and consumption per ton of steel produced.

In a meeting we had with the company's chief operating officer (COO), we asked when the senior executive team had last discussed energy KPIs and what results those meetings had produced. The COO paused for a moment, trying to remember. He finally replied that it had been more than a year and that no specific actions had been taken. The reason, he explained, was that no one could definitively explain what caused fluctuations in the KPIs.

Company leaders are responsible for their management systems and must drive the process of creating goals and KPIs that the entire organization can understand and act on. Indeed, leadership commitment is critical to keeping all three gears turning at the optimal speed. To make a transformation effort a success, business leaders need to devote time and energy to the effort beyond the technical challenges that are often at the top of executive agendas. Company leaders must focus unflinchingly on the business's culture and create management systems that turn goals into results. Leaders need to dedicate time to resource productivity by, for example, conducting line walks and performance-management discussions. Leadership commitment must be in the organization's vision and stated objectives. Only then can a company beat the daunting odds stacked against change programs.

Technical systems

In the context of resource-productive manufacturing, technical systems include all the equipment used to manufacture a product and the people and processes applied to them. As we discussed in Chapter 4 ("Think limits") companies need to understand the source and quantity of resource loss in the context of the system's theoretical limits.

By way of review, resource losses stem from two primary sources. The first is inherent is the system's design and includes faulty equipment that needs to be replaced, upgraded, or adapted. The second is operational issues, which often stem from employee failure to understand or adhere to procedures. However, in this chapter, we emphasize that even the most diligent analyses and standard operating procedures will fall flat if they aren't supported by management systems that set goals and accountabilities and a company culture that makes resource productivity a priority. We turn our attention to these challenges now.

Managing for resource productivity

For transformation efforts to succeed, companies must support them with a battery of formal management structures and systems that focus everyone's efforts. A compelling vision and carefully crafted goals are the starting point.

At the most fundamental level, a vision must capture the hearts and minds of employees; to do that, leaders must articulate an alluring future state of the business that people will buy into. Equally important, visions need to endure for several years. If they constantly change, the organization will become confused and often cynical about leadership's intentions, capabilities, and commitment.

Goals, on the other hand, are quite dynamic. Resource-productivity goals should be part of the annual budget and planning process. Goal setting is often most effective as a top-down exercise. Targets should be set at the corporate level and then broken down into subgoals for the site, plant, department, and team levels. At each tier, roles and accountabilities should be clearly defined and assigned.

Although goal setting is a top-down exercise, achieving those goals often relies on a vibrant bottom-up process anchored by KPIs, performance dialogues, and a culture of continuous improvement.

KPIs for resource productivity

When focused and precise, KPIs clearly measure progress and raise warning flags about potential issues that can hamper progress. To be an effective bulwark of performance management, KPIs need to meet the SMART criteria:

- **Specific:** Is the KPI straightforward, and can the company easily generate it?
- **Measurable:** Is the KPI easy to measure with available data? Can it be benchmarked against other teams, industry standards, or companies?
- **Actionable:** Can the team influence the KPI by understanding the drivers behind it?
- **Relevant:** Does the KPI clearly support high-level targets, including goals set at the corporate level?
- **Time bound:** Can the KPI be measured often enough to allow teams to address issues within the reporting cycle? Are the deadlines clear?

Creating SMART resource-productivity KPIs can be challenging because the metrics have to be normalized. As the COO of the steel manufacturer realized, many resource-productivity metrics in use today don't indicate the potential causes of variation in energy consumption at different points in time. Measures such as material or energy consumption per ton can be effective in understanding production in terms of variable costs. Any given process, however, has both constant and variable rates of energy consumption. The constant rates are not dependent on the volume of product produced. A certain amount of energy is consumed simply by having the facility available. By the same token, if production speed slows, more energy is consumed per ton of product than would be the case when production speeds are faster.

To normalize the data, KPIs should be based on the overall equipment effectiveness principles discussed in Chapter 4. When based on these principles, KPIs provide a complete picture of losses and their costs down to the day or even the hour. Specifically, KPIs should focus on energy loss that can be improved through better process controls:

- Quality—scrap and rework
- Availability—energy consumption when the line is down
- Product—differing energy needs for different products
- Load—losses when production speeds aren't optimal
- Performance—consumption above the optimal load curve

To drive a fine-tuned performance-management process, companies should develop leading and lagging KPIs to understand the consistency and impact of improvement efforts:

- **Leading:** What operators need to do to ensure the best results such as setting furnaces at the optimal temperature, or what maintenance engineers need to check on a regular basis such as compressed air leak prevalence.
- **Lagging:** The results of leading indicators and whether they are having the desired effect.

Performance dialogues

Performance dialogues are candid discussions of progress on KPIs and determine where teams need to focus. Because challenges and new ideas are part of the agenda, these conversations are a key inflection point in the bottom-up process of empowering teams to meet goals.

Mirroring the goal-setting process, performance dialogues should cascade through the company. For example, shift-level meetings should occur daily for 10 to 15 minutes to review the results of the day. Teams and their managers should meet weekly to address progress on performance improvements. Plant managers should meet monthly to review progress and vet new improvement efforts. Senior leaders should convene quarterly to chart progress, adjust goals, and understand where support is needed in order for the company to achieve its resource-productivity targets.

A culture of continuous improvement

To ensure the steady flow of fresh ideas, companies need to create a culture of continuous improvement. The management system should include processes that harness creativity and apply them rigorously to resource-productivity challenges. Engineers may be inspired by the quest to approach theoretical limits and organizations need to translate that enthusiasm into new ideas.

One approach is to tie people and teams to specific targets in areas such as water or energy use. Although this establishes responsibility and accountability, the company may still find that it needs a forum to nurture the creation of new approaches to energy efficiency.

Kaizen, the Japanese word for continuous improvement, is one of the most successful vehicles for continuous improvement. Also known as quality circles, Kaizen, in essence, consists of brainstorming sessions in which cross-functional teams assess a situation, identify challenges, and develop solutions. Depending on the nature of the challenge at hand, the length of these sessions can range from several hours to a few days, during which teams actually begin implementing their new ideas.

A major source of Kaizen's success is the root cause analysis it employs. People often gravitate towards the most apparent and straightforward solution to a challenge. However, that solution might not address the underlying issues that caused the problem. If a heat pump unexpectedly fails, for example, replacing it is a straightforward option. But it is also important to understand what caused the failure so as to prevent another one in the future. For example, the issue could be a supplier defect. But it could also be something under the company's control such as the liquid flowing through the pump.

A culture of continuous improvement lies at the heart of the bottom-up process of reaching resource-productivity goals. For the bottom-up efforts to take flight, employees must be empowered with enough latitude to drive projects on their own. Without that autonomy, motivation can evaporate very quickly.

Mind-sets, capabilities, and behaviors

Mind-sets, capabilities, and behaviors can make or break success. Peter Drucker, the well-known management thinker, once wryly quipped that culture eats strategy for breakfast. Even the most sophisticated technical plans and management infrastructures will produce disappointing, lackluster results if the company hasn't instilled the mind-sets that drive new behaviors.

In our experience, the process of changing behaviors typically moves through three phases (Exhibit 45).

In the first phase, employees are naturally skeptical. The resource-productivity program is still unproven, and employees will be reluctant to learn new tools and techniques that seem to be a competing priority. Through top-down pressure from executives and a team of change agents, companies experience a step change in the use of new tools and approaches. However, that step change is fragile. If organizations haven't successfully instilled mind-sets committed to resource productivity, the progress will stall at the level of achievement already gained. A truly committed workforce, on the other hand, will pick up the mantle and not revert to old habits.

Behaviors are easy to document because they are observable. For example, an organization can readily identify if people are using new tools. The underlying mind-sets, however, are more difficult to ferret out because they sit within the thoughts of individuals. To delve into the mind-sets at play, organizations can use any of the several tools at their disposal.

EXHIBIT 45

Knowledge and capabilities are needed to change employee behavior

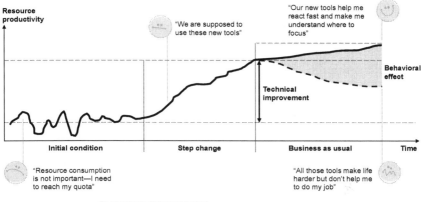

To sustain the behavioral effect
* Create awareness about resource productivity with your staff
* Train your staff on resource-productivity behavior
* Become a role model on resource productivity

SOURCE: McKinsey Resource-Productive Operations service line

Companywide surveys can uncover attitudes and quantify their presence across the enterprise. McKinsey has created an organizational health index for energy efficiency. Consisting of some 200 questions, the survey captures attitudes along nine dimensions including opinions about leadership, feelings about goals, and commitment to continuous improvement.

Extensive one-on-one interviews can probe attitudes more thoroughly. Lasting two to three hours, these sessions are conducted by trained interviewers who are skilled at unearthing what makes a person tick and the mind-sets that drive their current behaviors.

Mirror workshops are another powerful tool. In a mirror workshop, results from surveys and poignant quotes from interviews are placed on the walls like art in a gallery. Participants than view the material to develop a deep understanding of mind-sets and capabilities that need to change if new behaviors are to take hold.

A case in point: A chemical company surveys resource-productivity beliefs and practices

A European chemical company committed itself to resource-productivity transformation with a focus on non-capital-expenditure and lean initiatives. To identify any barriers standing in its way, the company fielded a survey to quantify attitudes about its practices. The organization also conducted extensive interviews to explore the underlying mind-sets.

The survey identified distinct areas for improvement. Although employees were committed to energy efficiency, for example, they felt that they weren't rewarded for achieving energy goals. Employees also didn't believe that the company had a continuous-improvement culture that encouraged them to develop and share new ideas.

Through extensive interviews, the organization discovered what employees thought were best practices as well as changes that needed to be made. Although buy-in to the vision was strong,

for example, it was checked by the belief that technology investment was the only way to realize energy savings. Employees did not understand the systemic sources of energy loss and improvements that could be achieved without new technologies.

In terms of KPIs, employees understood them. However, KPIs were only applied at the site and management levels. The company did not cascade the KPIs to the operator level in any actionable way. Moreover, the KPIs focused on historical performance instead of taking load effects into account.

Performance-review meetings were also limited to the senior ranks. Although these meetings were perceived as well run and based on candid fact-based debate, employees were frustrated that the organization did not consistently hold review meetings with operators and sometimes used e-mail for progress updates.

Moving forward

The analysis of mind-sets is the springboard for moving forward and changing behaviors. To be systematic, companies can use a formal influence model that moves them from insights into the current situation to management systems that drive and sustain new ways of working (Exhibit 46).

The process begins by disseminating information about the company's resource consumption and costs. The communication plan should include introductory training, which can be offered online. The training and communications should clearly describe what is expected of employees and how the coming changes will benefit the company and themselves.

After creating awareness of the initiative, the organization should start building skills and competencies. It should offer specialized training on specific issues and create committees and work groups responsible for various resource productivity challenges.

The influence model culminates in formal management systems and structures. With a staff that understands what is expected and is trained

Exhibit 46

EXHIBIT 46

Employees are more likely to change their behavior under four conditions

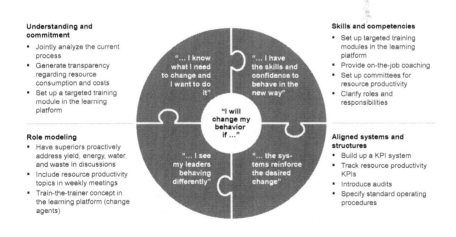

Understanding and commitment
- Jointly analyze the current process
- Generate transparency regarding resource consumption and costs
- Set up a targeted training module in the learning platform

Role modeling
- Have superiors proactively address yield, energy, water, and waste in discussions
- Include resource productivity topics in weekly meetings
- Train-the-trainer concept in the learning platform (change agents)

"... I know what I need to change and I want to do it"

"... I have the skills and confidence to behave in the new way"

"I will change my behavior if ..."

"... I see my leaders behaving differently"

"... the systems reinforce the desired change"

Skills and competencies
- Set up targeted training modules in the learning platform
- Provide on-the-job coaching
- Set up committees for resource productivity
- Clarify roles and responsibilities

Aligned systems and structures
- Build up a KPI system
- Track resource productivity KPIs
- Introduce audits
- Specify standard operating procedures

SOURCE: McKinsey analysis

in the tools that allow them to contribute, KPIs, standard operating procedures, and resource productivity audits will resonate. New behaviors will become the order of the day.

At the same time, management should clearly set standards by including resource productivity challenges in their discussions and convening weekly meetings to address resource-productivity issues. To build further momentum, the company should implement train-the-trainer workshops that develop a cadre of change agents with substantial knowledge of resource-productivity tools and approaches.

Building capabilities and know-how

As is the case with dedicated leadership support, skills and capabilities are needed to drive each gear in the transformation effort. These capabilities fall into three broad categories: technical know-how, soft skills, and management development. We describe each, including best practices, in the following section.

Technical know-how

The lack of tools and knowledge to analyze and improve technical systems is one of the main impediments to high-performing resource productivity. University engineering curricula, for example, rarely emphasize energy efficiency in a formal way. The common lack of knowledge of how to set up an effective steam system is an example of the gap. Engineers will study the thermodynamics of steam but aren't trained in the intricacies of a steam system such as the best placements of steam traps or how savings can be generated through better insulation. Companies have to take responsibility for developing this level of technical expertise. Creating expert groups can help fill skill gaps. Companies will often have experts in specific areas but few with well-rounded resource-productivity knowledge. To compensate, businesses can form a cross-functional team of experts that collectively provide a comprehensive view and support resource-productivity efforts across the organization.

Organizations should also consider creating the corporate-level role of process engineer. A senior-level subject-matter expert lessens the resource-specific technical demands of senior leaders for whom resource productivity is only part of their responsibilities.

"Soft skills"

So-called soft skills are extremely important although often downplayed as something that is "nice to have." However, performance dialogues require expert soft skills. If team leaders can't conduct effective meetings or lead candid exchanges of opinions and ideas, performance dialogues will become unproductive events that stall or even actively impede progress.

Essential soft skills include how to lead problem solving meetings, manage team performance, and give convincing presentations and make persuasive arguments. Because data are so important to resource productivity, companies should train managers and team leaders in data-visualization techniques and how to tell stories with data.

Management development

Experiential learning is proving to be one of the most enduring management training methods. Model factories are an effective venue to anchor experiential learning[24]. These factories are live operations with small lines and actual operators.

By working with live systems, managers can study resource issues in an actual setting that allows for experimentation and other forms of hands-on learning.

Companies should provide line managers with one or two days of training that introduces tools such as theoretical limits and profit per hour. Subject-matter experts, on the other hand, should be offered more comprehensive training such as field and forum programs. These programs convene a group of managers for several days of rigorous instruction in tools and techniques. Participants then go back into the field to implement a pilot. The group then reconvenes after a month or so to share results and experiences and to establish best practices.

---

24 McKinsey Capability Center Network, http://www.capability-center.mckinsey.com/.

Job shadowing is another approach. In job shadowing, a group of experts leads the team in an improvement effort. Then, the roles switch: the team takes the lead, coached by the experts. In the third phase, the pilot team becomes the experts and leads a new team at a different site, starting the process anew.

***

One-size-fits-all solutions don't drive successful change programs. When developing these programs, business leaders need to be cognizant of the unique corporate and national cultures that make up the DNA of their companies. A state-owned Chinese enterprise, for example, may rely more heavily on top-down approaches than bottom-up efforts. The DNA of a US company may be the opposite. European companies often fall somewhere in the middle.

Nonetheless, our research and experience has revealed clear building blocks that can help beat the daunting odds against successful transformation efforts: the three interlocking gears of technical systems, management infrastructure, and mind-sets, capabilities, and behaviors. When buttressed by leadership commitment and strong capabilities, these gears can help ensure that resource-productivity efforts achieve their desired results.

CHAPTER 7

THINK CIRCULAR

*T*o avoid running out of constrained resources, individuals and organizations taking part in the economy need to "think circular." This entails three key components: designing products for circularity, adopting new business models, and managing suppliers in new ways. Thinking circular builds on the advantages created by the preceding four core beliefs—think lean, think limits, think profit per hour, and think holistic—and serves as the ultimate step towards improving resource productivity.

A sobering scenario

Imagine the following scenario, described by Dame Ellen MacArthur—the fastest solo sailor to circumnavigate the globe and the leader of the Ellen MacArthur Foundation, which works with businesses, universities, and governments to accelerate the transition to a circular economy: you're setting off around the world on a boat. You have only so much food, fuel, and water. Days and then weeks into your trip, you watch your resources get depleted, and you realize how connected you feel to them. When your navigational aids tell you that you are 2,500 miles from the nearest human settlement, you fully grasp what the word finite means in terms of your very survival.

The global economy is no different. It is powered by resources that are ultimately finite. But it presents a challenge much greater than sailing around the world. To keep operating, the global economy relies on taking materials out of the ground and making them into other things. And those other things ultimately get thrown away. That is not sustainable in the long run. When you complete a journey around the world on a boat, you can stock up on fresh supplies of resources and set out again for the open seas. But you cannot do that on a global economic scale.[25]

Grasping the nuances of circular thinking

Thinking circular is all about fostering innovation and growth in manufacturing operations. The aim of thinking circular is to use fewer resources and to eradicate waste—not just in manufacturing processes, as lean management aspires to do, but throughout the life cycles and uses of products and their components. Indeed, in companies that think circular, what might otherwise be called waste often becomes valuable feedstock for subsequent usage steps.

Thinking circular requires a holistic approach applied across functions and all along the value chain (Exhibit 47). For instance, companies must set up their product designs and operational systems to fully support circularity, including the following:

- Sourcing of circular materials and inbound logistics
- Circular product design
- Operational improvement aimed at reducing required inputs and waste
- Marketing of circular products
- Financing for alternative business models
- Effective management of outbound logistics

Moreover, thinking circular is not the same as mere recycling. In fact, it's the repeated cycles of use and reuse, aided by the right product designs, that define circular thinking and distinguish it from recycling. With recycling, large amounts of embedded energy and labor are lost, materials are downgraded, and energy is needed to transform the materials into new products. With circularity, products and the materials they contain are kept in working condition as long as possible, reused or redistributed

---

25   Nguyen, Hanh, Martin Stuchtey, and Markus Zils: "Remaking the industrial economy," *mckinsey.com,* last modified February 2014, http://www.mckinsey.com/ insights/manufacturing/remaking_the_industrial_economy.

EXHIBIT 47

Thinking circular requires a holistic approach

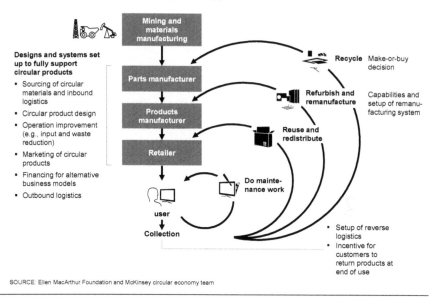

Designs and systems set up to fully support circular products

- Sourcing of circular materials and inbound logistics
- Circular product design
- Operation improvement (e.g., input and waste reduction)
- Marketing of circular products
- Financing for alternative business models
- Outbound logistics

Mining and materials manufacturing

Parts manufacturer

Products manufacturer

Retailer

user

Collection

Do maintenance work

Reuse and redistribute

Refurbish and remanufacture

Recycle

Recycle Make-or-buy decision

Refurbish and remanufacture Capabilities and setup of remanufacturing system

- Setup of reverse logistics
- Incentive for customers to return products at end of use

SOURCE: Ellen MacArthur Foundation and McKinsey circular economy team

when keeping them in working condition is not an option or no longer enough, refurbished or remanufactured, and then recycled as a last resort. Only when any remaining materials cannot be recycled or further used do they go to a landfill.

Circularity comes in different forms and degrees. Ideally, use-and-reuse cycles are kept as "tight" as possible. What do we mean by tight? The tighter the cycle, the less a product has to be changed in reuse, refurbishment, and remanufacturing and the faster it returns to use. More tightness means higher potential savings on the shares of material, labor, energy, and capital embedded in the product. An optimal degree of tightness also minimizes externalities such as greenhouse gas emissions, water, and toxicity.

In addition to "circling tighter," "circling longer" delivers important benefits. With every cycle, the originally sourced set of materials (and embedded labor and energy) deliver new, incremental value for the value

EXHIBIT 48

Comparing biological and technical materials "cradle to cradle" yields valuable insights

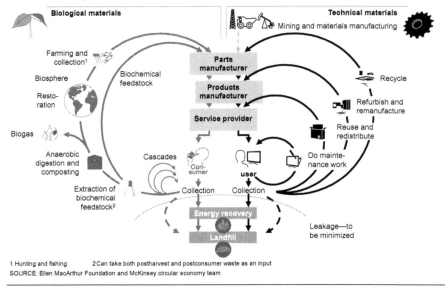

1 Hunting and fishing   2 Can take both postharvest and postconsumer waste as an input
SOURCE: Ellen MacArthur Foundation and McKinsey circular economy team

chain. Who captures that value depends on how supply chain participants are set up. Recycling value, for example, is very frequently not captured by the brand owner or manufacturer, even if these are the companies that push us on to higher recycling rates.

Circularity also makes a distinction between consumable and durable components of a product (Exhibit 48). From the circularity perspective, consumables are made largely of biological materials that can be returned to the biosphere, directly or through cascaded, consecutive uses. Durables, such as engines or computers, are made of technical materials unsuitable for the biosphere, like metals and plastics. These can be designed from the start for reuse.[26]

Tight and numerous cycles of use and reuse minimize leakage of value from the materials involved. For instance, leakage of biological

---

26   Ellen MacArthur Foundation, *Towards the Circular Economy: Economic and business rationale for an accelerated transition,* 2013, Volume 1, p. 3.

materials can take the form of lost opportunities to maximize reuse of materials before returning them to the soil, or the inability to restore materials to soil because they have become contaminated. Leakage of technical materials manifests itself as loss of materials, energy, and labor when products, components, and raw materials cannot be reused, refurbished, or recycled.

Understanding the challenge—and the benefits

As explained in Chapter 2, thinking circular requires making the mind-set shift from linear, "take, make, and dispose," "cradle to grave" supply chains to "take and restore," "cradle to cradle" supply circles. Companies that master this way of thinking—backed by powerful practices and tools comparable to lean manufacturing—behave very differently from those trapped in the supply chain mentality. For one thing, they manage their products as their future resources. They also broaden their thinking about their business models. In addition, they collaborate internally and externally to optimize the overall supply circle in which they participate.

Businesses that successfully make this shift can reap rewards in such forms as cost savings, revenue upside, and strategic repositioning. This potential exists in areas such as mining and materials-manufacturing companies, parts manufacturers, product makers, retailers, or collection and sorting enterprises.

Consider these examples:

- **Cost savings:** Lend Lease reduced material volume by using scaffolding wood from the construction process to furnish and landscape the London Olympic Village.[27] Bosch reduced material price volatility by bringing material back into its product at previously agreed prices.
- **Revenue upside:** Vodafone captured premium pricing and stabilized market-share dilution through non-sales-based services.

---

27   Ellen MacArthur Foundation, *Towards the Circular Economy: Accelerating the scale-up across global supply chains,* 2014, Volume 3, p. 46.

Its Red Hot program, for instance, requires customers to turn in their old phones when they want to receive new models. That way, Vodafone can recover value from the old ones, and program participants can gain access to the latest phone designs.[28]

- **Strategic repositioning:** Teijin created a strategic lock-in with apparel maker Patagonia by developing a proprietary process for recycling polyester.[29] Philips staved off potential EU eco-design regulations and set itself a target to use 3,500 tons of recycled plastic in 2015.[30]

Thinking circular positions companies to win in these other ways as well[31]:

- Reduced material bills and warranty risks through reselling and component recovery.
- Improved customer interaction, as companies generate more customer insights by deploying new business models such as leasing versus selling.
- Stronger customer loyalty, as companies use customer insights to personalize offerings.
- Less product-portfolio complexity and more manageable life cycles through development of stable product "kernels" that companies can augment with changeable add-ons.

With such meaningful benefits and with telltale signs of resource bottlenecks becoming increasingly hard to ignore, the call for a new economic model is growing. The concept of a circular economy is capturing the attention of CEOs at leading companies in a wide range of sectors.

---

28 Ellen MacArthur Foundation, *Towards the Circular Economy: Accelerating the scale-up across global supply chains,* 2014, Volume 3, p. 17.

29 Patagonia, http://www.patagonia.com/us/footprint/read-the-story/?assetid=68388.

30 Philips, "Closing the Materials Loop," *philips.com,* 2014, http://www.philips.com/about/sustainability/ourenvironmentalapproach/greeninnovation/closingthematerialsloop.page.

31 Ellen MacArthur Foundation, *Towards the Circular Economy: Economic and business rationale for an accelerated transition,* 2013, Volume 1, p. 9.

EXHIBIT 49

Companies can become sustainable by choice, not just by compliance

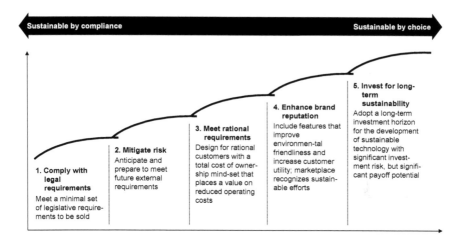

Sustainable by compliance ▶ Sustainable by choice ▶

1. Comply with legal requirements
Meet a minimal set of legislative requirements to be sold

2. Mitigate risk
Anticipate and prepare to meet future external requirements

3. Meet rational requirements
Design for rational customers with a total cost of ownership mind-set that places a value on reduced operating costs

4. Enhance brand reputation
Include features that improve environmen-tal friendliness and increase customer utility; marketplace recognizes sustainable efforts

5. Invest for long-term sustainability
Adopt a long-term investment horizon for the development of sustainable technology with significant investment risk, but significant payoff potential

SOURCE: McKinsey analysis

Rising and increasingly volatile input costs alone are creating strong incentives to minimize the virgin material and energy content of companies' product designs. In Europe, for instance, analysts forecast a 47 percent increase in carbon-permit prices by 2015.[32]

Moreover, new stakeholders are gaining influence. To illustrate, campaigning by environmentally focused nongovernmental organizations has played a decisive role in encouraging consumer-packaged-goods companies to move away from using palm oils in their products. As poor environmental performance becomes unacceptable, companies that demonstrate greater responsibility have much to gain. Those that move from "sustainable by compliance" to "sustainable by choice" will especially benefit from a strengthened brand image (Exhibit 49).[33] With these

32   Reuters, Thomson: "Analysts raise carbon price forecasts," *Point Carbon News,* July 8, 2013.
33   Hannon, Eric, and Stephan Mohr: "Future-proofing: Taking the long view on sustainable product development (part 1 of 2)," McKinsey & Company Operations Extranet, March 2014.

developments in mind, let's take a closer look at the first core element in thinking circular: designing products for circularity.

Designing products for circularity

Designing products for circularity[34] or resource productivity (DfRPS – Design for Resource Productive Systems) means developing them in ways that require less nonrenewable resources and materials and lower-cost inputs, which in turn leads to lower operating costs (including energy usage) and less capital employed. Such products provide more value to the consumer because many of them are cheaper to own and use. Increased value can be reflected in higher pricing-further improving profitability for the company.

Tracking energy consumption through the product life cycle

All of this can be summed up as designing products with the future in mind. That includes choices not only about which manufacturing inputs a company will use but also how the product will be transported to customers, how customers will use it, and how its materials will eventually be reused as the basis for new products.

Energy consumption is a big factor here. Many companies already consider this during production, but they don't look holistically at such consumption throughout their product's entire life cycle. As energy prices rise, for example, transportation costs will make up an ever larger share of a product's overall cost.

This idea of looking at the total cost of a product-upfront costs as well as ongoing costs—is already well established in the business-to-business (B2B) marketplace. We expect that attention to total cost will become pervasive in the business-to-consumer (B2C) realm as well, as product information becomes more readily available to consumers through online comparison services or regulatory labeling.

---

34 Hannon, Eric, and Stephan Mohr: "Future-proofing: Taking the long view on sustainable product development (part 1 of 2)," McKinsey & Company Operations Extranet, March 2014.

A case in point: Redesigning equipment at a heavy-equipment manufacturer

A heavy-equipment manufacturer designed and planned a resource-productivity transformation program that included rethinking its forklift trucks to make the vehicles more cost competitive and environmentally friendly. The "design to green" effort centered on reducing the vehicles' weight. The reason was that the volume of carbon emissions is directly linked to weight: heavier vehicles need to burn more fuel to operate, leading to higher fuel costs and greater volumes of carbon emissions.

The newly designed truck weighed 2,800 kilograms, an 8 percent decrease from the 3,000 kilograms that the older, heavier model weighed. The company also saved 2 percent in cost of goods sold, because of material cost reduction. And, customers who bought the forklift truck saved considerably on fuel-some of them to the tune of 3,000 liters over its 15,000 hour product life.

Considering product end of life

End-of-life considerations for a product—which will be subject to more stringent government regulations—are also important in design for resource-productive systems. Companies need to maximize reuse of product materials so that more material can become raw material for the next generation of products. As a quick example, consider the Espresso Mushroom Company, which collects used coffee grounds and uses them as a substrate for growing high-quality mushrooms. The company also supplies kits that enable consumers to use the same process to recycle coffee grounds at home. As the mushrooms grow, they dry out the coffee grounds, producing a valuable soil enhancer.[35]

---

35   Espresso Mushroom Company, http://espressomushroom.co.uk/environment/.

One savvy end-of-life approach is to use modular product designs that allow the exchange of key functional modules or components. The mobile phone industry is already experimenting with such an approach in designs like Motorola's Project Ara.[36] Such designs make the product easy to upgrade as new technologies or features become available, rather than being abandoned for another design. When a product does reach the end of its life or is damaged, modularity also allows components to be removed and used as repair parts for other products. In addition, it can simplify the separation of raw materials for recycling.

Designing right—from the start

The most critical decisions contributing to circular product design are made early in the development process. When a design is "frozen," most of the product's future environmental footprint is already defined. Thus, choices about materials, manufacturing processes, operating efficiencies, repair, reuse, refurbishment, and recycling ease can't be readily altered later on. For products with long life cycles, noncircular design choices will create long-lasting burdens for the company.

To make effective design decisions early in the process, companies need to broaden their circle of stakeholders involved in product development. In many companies, the product development group already works with marketing to define traditional customer-related requirements. To design products for circularity, they will also need to work with other internal functions—business development, R&D, regulatory, supply chain, production—to gather current and potential requirements for new business models, and with regulatory agencies, logistics companies, after-sales services, disposal and recycling companies, and other end-of-life value-recovery businesses. CEOs or chief operating officers (COOs) may have to take on a convening role, because representatives from these diverse functions need to work together in new ways to provide ideas for the best ways to design products.

---

36 Smith, Chris: "Motorola's Project Ara modular Phone prototype is 'almost ready'," *techradar. phones,* December 7, 2013, http://www.techradar.com/news/phone-and-communications/mobile-phones/motorola-s-project-ara-modular-phone-prototype-isalmost-ready--1205753.

Spotlight on steel: Shifting focus from emissions to metal flows

Beyond efficiency and recycling in steel, it's time to master the art of circularity. Consider this: the demand for steel will likely double in the next 40 years—but the industry is seeking to reduce CO_2 emissions steeply in that same time frame. Most energy is used in upstream liquid-metal production, and recycling rates are already among the highest of all recycled products.

The obvious solution is for industry players to focus on factors affecting emissions. But the industry is already recycling massively, while seeking every possible energy-efficiency opportunity, and those efforts are close to the theoretical limit. Electric arc furnaces, for example, are getting closer to what can be achieved. The steel industry started the ultra-low-CO_2 steel program to work on breakthrough technologies. (The first plant that potentially could recover useful energy out of heat from slag is currently being constructed.) Greater use of clean electricity is another option, but renewables are diffuse in terms of power per land-area unit.

We believe that industry players could make much greater progress through circularity, specifically by focusing on the flow of metal through the value chain (though care has to be taken in defining the business model). Reuse of steel in the construction industry—a huge consumer of raw materials—is already under way, and the availability of reused steel is rapidly improving in the United Kingdom. Moreover, steel manufacturers could reuse old metal in casting processes, as well as divert metal from rolling and forming operations. To illustrate, they could trim and sell sheet and plate skeletons and sell to the market for overordered stock. Finally, steel fabricators could use less of these materials in their designs. For example, manufacturers of steel I-beams can apply lightweight design principles to create beams that support multiple loads together and to optimize beams' cross-section for bending. These and other practices could enable companies to reduce the amount of steel required in a product by as much as 30 to 40 percent while giving them a competitive edge. Such strategies could collectively lead to as much as a 50 percent reduction in CO_2 emissions in the industry overall, as well as lower manufacturers' costs, thereby improving their bottom line.

Source:

Allwood, Julian M. "Sustainable Materials with Both Eyes Open," University of Cambridge, 2012.

Building on designing for cost and designing for value

DfRPS provides value to a broad group of stakeholders by taking a longer view of consumption and using circular-economy thinking. It builds on two other frequently used approaches: design to cost, which focuses on delivering products at minimum cost to maximize the company's bottom line, and design to value, which concentrates on delivering more value to customers at minimum. DfRPS helps companies design products that deliver long-term value to a broader set of stakeholders—maximizing the company's top line for a given amount of resources. It also exerts a bottom-line impact; for instance, by reducing cost of goods sold. It rests on a bold premise: that the most resource-efficient solutions are also the optimal economic solutions in the long run.

The following tips can help companies use DfRPS to build on the advantages offered by designing for cost and value.

Understand new options

Gain familiarity with new design solutions available to your company, new "multilife" material options, and new product-development and manufacturing technologies such as injection molding and 3-D printing. By leveraging new options, you can replace incremental, small improvements in product design with breakthrough changes that dramatically boost circularity. Examples include designing for easy disassembly and replacing machined parts made through the removal of material (which produces waste) with injection-molded parts made with very little waste.

A case in point: High tech goes circular

The meteoric rise of server-based services and the Internet in the past 15 years has not only revolutionized the way we do business, built fortunes, and fundamentally restructured social interaction, it has also created a whole new demand for electricity and the resources required to make the Web function. From a tiny blip on the resource screen in the mid-1990s, IT departments (and especially data centers) are now a measurable user of energy that is growing in leaps and bounds around the world. Consider:

- Electricity consumed by data centers worldwide increased by 19 percent from 2011 to 2012.
- Data centers now consume approximately 3 percent of the world's energy production, accounting for about 200 million metric tons of CO_2 emissions.

In addition, growing costs, capacity constraints, and heightened customer awareness of the impact on climate change have been converging to threaten historical business models.

One global data-services company recognized both the threat and the opportunity to demonstrate how circular thinking and integrated design could revolutionize the way data centers were designed and operated. To do so, it reached well beyond its own 130,000-person workforce to bring in leading thinkers from around the globe from disparate industries including server manufacturers; military equipment providers; heating, ventilation, and air-conditioning designers; lighting experts; software developers; backup-power suppliers; and those versed in customer sales and marketing.

The results were spectacular. The team designed and built a facility that reduced energy consumption by 80 percent while keeping capital requirements constant. More important, the dramatic increase in efficiency—measured in power-utilization efficiency—meant that 82 percent of incoming electricity was used for data services, which in turn meant 80 percent more revenue potential than offered by an equivalent-sized facility using standard linear approaches.

The same company then went on to identify 20 percent more capacity in its existing facilities, meaning that a planned program for data center expansion could be slowed, generating a savings (in net present value) of USD 200 million.

Sources:

- Datacenter Dynamics, "DCD Industry Census 2013: Data Center Power," 2013, http://www.datacenterdynamics.com/focus/archive/2014/01/dcd-industry-census-2013-data-center-power; accessed April 7, 2014.

- Rallo Aaron: "Interview by Data Center Journal Q&A," Industry Outlook: Data Center Energy Efficiency, March 5, 2014, http://www.datacenter-journal.com/it/industry-out-look-data-center-energy-effi-ciency/; accessed April 7, 2014.

- StorageServers, "Facts and Stats of World's Largest Data Centers," July 17, 2013, http://storageservers.wordpress.com/2013/07/17/facts-and-stats-of-worlds-largest-data-centers/; accessed April 7, 2014.

Make smart trade-offs

Top-line impact from DfRPS comes from higher value delivered to customers, most often through reducing the total cost of ownership of a product. But at every stage of the product-design process, you'll need to make trade-offs between customers' desire for product performance and the resource-efficient production, operation, and circle closure to maximize value creation. Typical questions for a coffee-machine manufacturer could be the following: "Would an energy-efficient coffee machine get a high enough price premium to offset the extra production cost?" "Would ground-bean efficiency get a high enough price premium to offset the extra production cost?" "What is the most common failure and would the value generated from the spare piece to repair this failure offset the cost of offering the spare piece or losing a new sale?" and so on.

Foster the transparency of resource consumption

Make sure stakeholders understand the total resource consumption that a product requires, across its many life cycles. Across the product life cycle, identify the high-impact levers you want to target for sustainability optimization. As the product's design progresses, continually refine it based on this transparency, to ensure that the final configuration is sustainable, circular, and profitable. Consider all criteria affecting sustainability, circularity, and profitability—such as material, energy, labor, equipment, repair/reuse/refurbish/recycle options, and overhead costs; number of units sold; after-sales business; price premium; and cost of goods sold, which ultimately affects the bottom line.

Build relevant expertise

Encourage the hiring of managers from outside the company to bring in the right talent. Invest in technologies (such as 3-D printing for rapid prototyping) that can help in your DfRPS effort. Build capabilities in approaches such as reverse engineering (of competitors' products), which enables you to find out which materials are used in the products, how many parts a product has, how parts are assembled, and level of repairability/reusability/refurbishability/recyclability of parts and materials. Develop a discipline in monitoring advances and trends in new material types and new manufacturing techniques such 3-D printing, remanufacturing technologies (diagnostics, cleaning, refinishing), and tracking technologies. In addition, look at what you are already doing in this space in other parts of the organization. To illustrate, if a department is already engaged in some form of circularity, its quality-control employees probably already have a protocol for inspecting harvested parts. You may be able to leverage that protocol in other business units that want to "go circular."

Adopting new business models

Companies that adopt new business models supporting circular thinking seek to maintain ownership of the resources embedded in their offerings and view themselves as selling performance rather than

A case in point: ARM makes a strategic trade-off—and turns resource productivity into competitive advantage

In 2002, UK semiconductor designer ARM Holdings had mostly disappeared from the PC and server markets, which Intel and AMD had come to dominate. The latter two giants were locked in a battle to rapidly increase processing speed. However, as the battle heated up, the big players largely ignored the issue of energy consumption, and their chips became noticeably power hungry.

Sensing a shift in market needs, ARM made the strategic decision to continue developing chips that, while slower, proved extremely power efficient. The company made the decision before the advent of the smartphone and before a market for efficient chips had taken root. Towards the end of the decade, as smartphones became more sophisticated, handset sales burgeoned globally. And as the line between phone and computer blurred, demand soared for chips with very low power consumption—because they preserve battery life.

By the end of 2011, ARM dominated the market, shipping 90 percent of the roughly half-billion processors for smartphones worldwide.[37] Had the company not made this strategic trade-off, the scale-up and innovations in mobile devices and services would have happened later. At the same time, the decision created more value for customers and higher profitability for mobile-device makers.

products. Such business models enable companies to reduce costs, capture new sources of revenue, and forge closer bonds with customers that lead to greater insight into customers' wants and needs.

Moving from a selling to a leasing or service-provision arrangement with customers is an increasingly common business model change that

---

37 ARM (2003, 2012); Gartner (2012); In-Stat (2003); iSuppli (2012); Strategy Analytics (2010, 2012).

supports circularity. Leasing has long been used in the B2B world. For instance, for large equipment, service contracts have proved quite profitable for the companies offering them, as well as valuable for customers. Leasing trucks by distances driven is one example that truck OEMs and suppliers have already implemented.

Though leasing has proved its mettle for large equipment B2B companies, there is considerable untapped potential in the small-equipment B2B world (for example, companies that make electrical drives) and the B2C realm. To capture this potential, companies need to build on past success stories and drive this business model into new areas. In the area of B2C, examples of pioneers include leasing batteries in electric cars or asking customers to return the batteries once they're finished with them.

A case in point: Rolls-Royce pioneers Power-by-the-Hour

In 1962, Rolls-Royce, a global power-systems company, created its Power-by-the-Hour service to support the Viper engine on the de Havilland/Hawker Siddeley 125 business jet. The company offered a complete engine-and-accessory-replacement service on a fixed-cost-per-flying-hour basis. Manufacturers and operators paid only for engines that performed well. In 2002, Rolls-Royce introduced its CorporateCare service, which offered additional features. These included engine-health monitoring, which tracks on-wing performance using onboard sensors; lease-engine access to replace an operator's engine during off-wing maintenance, thereby minimizing downtime; and a global network of authorized maintenance centers to support customers as needed. The service mitigates risks to operators related to unscheduled maintenance events and makes maintenance costs planned and predictable.

Source:
Rolls-Royce, "Rolls-Royce celebrates 50th anniversary of Power-by-the-Hour," press release, October 30, 2012, http://www.rolls-royce.com/news/press_releases/2012/121030_the_Hour.jsp; accessed July 23, 2014.

In B2C, the appliance industry—for instance, the manufacture of washing machines—provides an example of an as yet untapped opportunity. Washing machines contain valuable materials, including metals from the appliances' housing and copper wiring used in the motors. A company that makes and sells such appliances loses control over those materials every time a consumer buys one. When the machine comes to the end of its life—breaks down, wears out— the customer who bought it disposes of it and buys another one, potentially from a different company.

Contrast that scenario with one in which the company sets up an end-of-life contract with customers and leases the washing machine to them. Through this business model, the company takes back the old machine and replaces it with a new or refurbished one, all the while maintaining ownership of the materials in the product. The manufacturer can decide whether to refurbish used machines it takes back and then lease or sell them out to the market—all options that are much cheaper in terms of required capital expenditure than designing and building brand-new machines. In fact, maintaining versus manufacturing a new machine can reduce the cost of capital for the manufacturer by as much as 5 percent.

Think about it: by refurbishing a washing machine—replacing the more fragile parts such as bearings and heating elements—companies incur lower production costs and return refreshed machines to the market faster, so the equipment can start making money for them sooner. Furthermore, when the machines are designed for easy maintenance and refurbishment, they may be recirculated back through the market many, many times—making them (in a sense) immortal. Indeed, with this business model, enhanced profit potential could come from numerous directions (Exhibit 50).

Clearly, companies can win big by switching from selling products to selling performance. But the customer also wins. In the washing machine example, consumers don't care about owning laundry equipment: they want clean clothes. A leasing arrangement would get them a hassle-free cleaning service: if the machine breaks, they get another one. Moreover, manufacturers could leverage the Internet of Things, defined as a scenario in which objects, animals, or people are provided with unique identifiers and the ability to transfer data over a network without requiring human-to-human or human-to-computer interaction. Such managers could

EXHIBIT 50

Leasing washing machines could uncover new wellsprings of profit

ILLUSTRATIVE

XX % Increase in profit potential

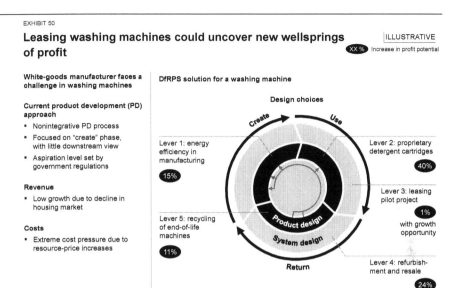

White-goods manufacturer faces a challenge in washing machines

Current product development (PD) approach
- Nonintegrative PD process
- Focused on "create" phase, with little downstream view
- Aspiration level set by government regulations

Revenue
- Low growth due to decline in housing market

Costs
- Extreme cost pressure due to resource-price increases

DfRPS solution for a washing machine

Design choices

Create   Use

Product design
System design

Return

Lever 1: energy efficiency in manufacturing — 15%

Lever 2: proprietary detergent cartridges — 40%

Lever 3: leasing pilot project — 1% with growth opportunity

Lever 5: recycling of end-of-life machines — 11%

Lever 4: refurbishment and resale — 24%

SOURCE: McKinsey Resource-Productive Operations service line

install inexpensive sensors that send alerts to manufacturers or service companies, letting them know that a part or component will soon need servicing or replacement, or that the machine overall will soon need refurbishing. That way, the company can take the appropriate action—before the appliance breaks down and the customer is inconvenienced.

In addition, appliance manufacturers could provide further value by selling cartridges filled with detergent selected to be environmentally friendly and the right match for a particular customer's level of water hardness. These are much less costly than the machines themselves for the company to manufacture and could deliver a major increase in profit potential. They further benefit consumers by helping them avoid the all-too-common tendency towards using more detergent than is needed to get their clothes clean—saving them money in the long run.

The leasing arrangement also leads to more frequent interactions with the customer, during which the company gains more data and insights for further improving its products and services. Even more important, it avoids the next "moment of truth" purchasing decision (or, at a minimum, can control the moment of truth more effectively because the company is better informed about when it will occur). Thus, there is less risk of losing the customer to the competition at the next purchase, because the company has had plenty of time to prepare him or her for that moment. What's more, the company doesn't have to renegotiate pricing each time it does business with a customer. As a result, it can foster longterm relationships with customers.

Spotlight on capital requirements

New business models are all about boosting profit per product. However, shareholder value is determined more by return on invested capital (ROIC) or return on capital employed. Thus, companies must also include capital requirements in their valuation of a new business model under consideration. That means taking into account the effect of capital shareholder-value creation or the business model a company currently has in use.

Take equipment servicing after installation to ensure reliable operations. The revenue basis is smaller, but margins are higher, and minimal capital is required. Thus, the ROIC is good. This kind of thinking is already widespread among industrial equipment providers that are actively moving into after-sales services. The challenge is to extend it to companies in other sectors—such as fast-moving consumer goods—where cost per piece is smaller. Adopting a model for piece maintenance—whereby a company not only sells products but also maintains and refurbishes them—could hold promise.

In addition to B2C, new business models can help mining and materials companies think circular as well. Consider copper mines, which could sell high-voltage electrical-transmission copper wires through a leasing arrangement that requires the return of the wire at the end of the life cycle of the copper product. The mine would thus retain ownership of the copper along the entire value chain, versus having recovery of wires handled by other companies.

Collaborating with suppliers in new ways

Some companies' supply chains are responsible for much of the company's environmental impact. To illustrate, roughly 50 percent of a pharmaceutical company's environmental impact in terms of carbon footprint stems from operations outside its four walls, including suppliers and logistics providers as well as customers' use and disposal of products. Once a company has designed its products for circularity and adopted new business models that support circularity, it needs to "complete the circle" by managing its suppliers in ways that enable them to become more efficient so as to save materials and energy while closing the loop. To manage suppliers in such ways, businesses must consider multiple aspects of supply chain management, such as procurement, return logistics, and remanufacturing.

We've identified four possible levers to improve circularity in a company's supply chain through supplier collaboration:

- Leveraging your purchasing power
- Exchanging information with your suppliers
- Using clean-sheet redesign
- Spearheading improvements with your suppliers

Leveraging your purchasing power

Use your purchasing power and purchasing insights to help your suppliers locate more sustainable sourcing options for their raw materials and energy. It also helps them access energy resources that exert a smaller environmental impact. This could include the joint purchasing of electricity so that carbon-neutral electricity can be sourced at the price of green electricity, or helping to select the right company to provide more sustainable semifinished products. In addition, consider providing your suppliers with less expensive access to capital to improve their existing operations. Funding the installation of combined-cycle gas turbines with waste-heat recovery for steam production is one example. Another is the installation of low-grade waste-heat recovery or biogas production from waste-water technologies. Small players in many industries have difficulty making a sound business case for such technologies when using their own cost of capital.

Exchanging information with your suppliers

Exchange more information about sales forecasting and stock levels with your suppliers to reduce the occurrence of empty loads in the distribution of your products. Better information sharing can also help you to avoid inventory waste. For example, sharing your long-and short-term sales forecast and inventory levels can help suppliers to produce what is expected and avoid the overproduction that often leads to obsolescence. In addition, sharing this type of information opens opportunities to shorten your planning trajectories from weeks to just days.

Information sharing can also help suppliers identify new technologies that would allow them increase circularity—for example, by increasing the amount of recycled material in a product, or identifying consumers that can be a source of more refurbishable/recyclable material.

Additionally, companies can help their suppliers in setting up tracking systems that create more transparency regarding their circularity and footprint (for both the company and the supplier).

Using clean-sheet redesign

Through clean-sheet redesign, you and your suppliers can collaborate to increase the value for customers of the product or service offered while minimizing requirements for resources and capital, including more circular designs such as repair/ reuse/refurbish/recycle. Start by selecting raw materials from renewable or recycled sources and using low-resource manufacturing technologies, such as mass-conserving part shaping (for example, injection molding) and nonpermanent assembly processes. Then consider alternative circular-business models—for example, you can utilize reusable packaging and locate the supply chain closer to the customer. In another example, a pharmaceutical company can work with its suppliers to redesign the devices used to administer medications, such as inhalers, so that less material is required (design-to-cost) or so that recycled plastics can be utilized.

Spearheading improvements with your suppliers

Help your suppliers increase energy efficiency and yield, which translates into use of less material. A 10 percent energy-efficiency improvement in your supply chain, which can make up 10 to 50 percent of your supply chain cost and is often half the cost of your product, could subsequently improve your net margin by 0.5 to 2.5 percent, assuming full value is captured (claiming all savings versus sharing them with suppliers). Renault discovered this firsthand. The company had been procuring cutting oils used in its machining centers from the cutting equipment manufacturer. Servicing as well as disposal of the oils was done by Renault. Fluid was exchanged weekly or monthly owing to impurities, creating significant waste. Renault asked the machine manufacturer to provide maintenance services for the cutting equipment, including fluid supply and disposal. The supplier extended the usage period to a full year owing to improved design of fluid and usage processes. Renault's total cost of ownership dropped by 20 percent while the supplier has and continues to move up the value chain to become more profitable.[38]

Working with suppliers to improve energy efficiency can also move companies a long way towards ISO compliance, which may soon become a prerequisite for certain customers, particularly government agencies and institutions.[39]

Towards this end, extend the scope of your supplier-development efforts to include circularity. For instance, arrange for resource-efficiency experts to review and improve your suppliers' operations, jointly invest in resource-efficient equipment, or share databases or IT tools.

∗ ∗ ∗

To stay ahead of the resource revolution, manufacturers can no longer solely rely on improving their resource efficiency. There's only so much more they can do on that front. In the heavy industry sector, for example, players can squeeze perhaps only 10 to 20 percent more efficiency out of their energy usage, even when investing in large capital expenditures.

---

38 Nguyen, Hanh, Martin Stuchtey, and Markus Zils: "Remaking the industrial economy," *mckinsey.com,* last modified February 2014, http://www.mckinsey.com/ insights/manufacturing/ remaking_the_industrial_economy.

39 Bennette, Nick, Markus Hammer, and Steven Swartz: "Tools for sustainability: How and why to work with supply chains on energy efficiency," to be published by McKinsey's Sustainability and Resource-Productivity Practice, autumn 2014.

Spotlight on supplier engagement

Engaging with suppliers in new ways to foster sustainability in their supply chain isn't new. But participants in a McKinsey survey agreed that such efforts could be more effective. Current approaches involve subjecting suppliers to questionnaires, inspections, audits, and scorecards. These are one-way information flows from the supplier to its customer only, and thus don't help suppliers execute improvements.

Leading companies are looking to develop two-way information-sharing and engagement models that benefit both sides.

Companies are adopting additional effective approaches as well. Take retail giant Walmart. A member of the Sustainability Consortium, which comprises more than a hundred companies, universities, and nongovernmental organizations, Walmart long ago acknowledged the importance of its supply chain footprint, which accounts for many times more greenhouse gas emissions than its own operations. It worked with the Environmental Defense Fund to set a goal of cutting supply-chain emissions by 20 million metric tons by 2015, in large part by capturing energy-efficiency opportunities. In addition to working with the Carbon Disclosure Project and developing its own product sustainability index, Walmart started a Supplier Energy Efficiency Program (SEEP). Through SEEP, experts audit supplier sites and then suggest improvements, such as lighting retrofits and automated building-control systems, that have worked well in Walmart's own facilities.

If your company has a sizable supplier network—comprising, say, tens of thousands of individual facilities—you need an approach that combines the scalability and reach offered by supplier score-carding with the factory-level focus demonstrated by Walmart's SEEP initiative. These tips can help:

- Identify supply chain elements to focus on. Assess your purchased product or service categories to determine which are most energy intensive and could provide the best savings opportunities. For instance, a company that makes footwear might find that suppliers providing fabric dyeing, cutting and sewing, and resin manufacturing could achieve the best savings in energy consumption.

- Develop a two-way engagement model. List relevant improvement projects for each product or service category you're focused on, by working with a small initial subset of suppliers or using tools such as the supplier-collaboration version of the RedE (resource efficiency deployment engine) Web-based platform. (Visit *https://apps.mckinsey.com/ RedE/*to learn more about the supplier-engagement version of the RedE tool, which supports such information sharing and engagement.) Build case models where suppliers can estimate their own capital requirements for such projects and quantify the financial benefit of their efforts.

- Get started. Test the engagement model with a subset of supportive suppliers that are drawn from each product or service category and that will help refine the model and any tools used. Then, scale up in category-by-category waves, allowing for a focus on category-specific improvement levers. For example, a footwear company's cut-and-sew suppliers could provide feedback on which levers are most effective and what additional improvements they have or would like to pursue. Roll out this iterative process to all your target suppliers.

- Get your peers involved. Use peer pressure to encourage other buyers to engage their supply chains, too. According to the Carbon Disclosure Project, just under half of suppliers that receive a reporting request from a single buyer company comply with the request. Three-quarters of those that receive requests from two or more companies will respond.

Source:
Bennette, Nick, Markus Hammer, and Steven Swartz, "Tools for sustainability: How and why to work with supply chains on energy efficiency," to be published by McKinsey's Sustainability and Resource-Productivity Practice, autumn 2014.

For this reason, we maintain that circular thinking—maximizing the renewal of increasingly scarce materials used in production operations—constitutes the best means of capturing the resource-productivity prize. As with the other core beliefs covered in the preceding chapters, fostering a "think circular" mind-set and practices throughout an organization is a process—one that requires patience and careful attention to change management. The fact that many government agencies are providing incentives focused on reducing labor and capital costs—not on making better use of raw materials—does not make the matter any easier.

With such challenges in mind, we lead you to the next section of this book, which provides a road map for realizing your resource-productive operations (RPO) vision. In the following three chapters, you'll discover how to prepare for an RPO-focused corporate-transformation journey, optimize a manufacturing site at your organization, and take actions now to get your organization started.

PART 3
THE ROAD MAP FOR SUCCESS

Implementing the five core beliefs requires a sizable change-management effort. More than just upgrading the facilities, it requires revamping the way your company is organized as well, with new roles and responsibilities for key stakeholders, and new tools, tactics, and processes. In addition, this transformation is an ongoing evolution that is never truly finished. Yet there are clear steps that a company should take to push the odds significantly in their favor.

CHAPTER 8

PREPARING FOR THE CORPORATE-TRANSFORMATION JOURNEY

B oosting resource productivity requires a major change effort that un-folds over time and is never finished. A company will need to alter its operating system. But that's just the beginning. To set the stage for a successful transformation journey, it must master several prerequisites in addition to instilling the five core beliefs discussed in Section 2. These prerequisites include alignment of top management; the right management infrastructure; a strong communication plan; and the development of required mind-sets, capabilities, and behaviors. How a company approaches each prerequisite will differ depending on its circumstances. But manufacturers that take the right approach can skew the odds that their new operating system will deliver the promised gains.

Aligning top management
A change effort aimed at improving resource productivity in manufacturing operations can succeed only if top management is aligned behind the program. This is true whether the change program is mandated "from the top down" by high-level executives or fueled by site managers who have been inspired by what they've learned about the advantages of resource productivity and who need top management's backing to support the effort. In either case, the transformation is implemented in multiple waves through a powerful combination of top-down planning and restructuring along with bottom-up rollout of the new operating system.

In a company where a resource-productivity program is driven from the top, the effort often involves several stages (Exhibit 51). In the first stage, a pilot improvement program is conducted at a selected manufacturing site, which can take several months. In the second stage, altered operations are rolled out among the company's production sites, typically over 12 to 18 months. In the third stage, which can occur in parallel with stages one and two, the company organizes for continuous improvement of manufacturing operations, which may include setting up a new business unit in charge of this process. Below, we take a closer look at each stage and consider top management's role as the transformation journey unfolds.

Pilot program

Top management may mandate a pilot program aimed at improving resource productivity at a selected production site, sometimes with the support of external experts. Leaders at the company's headquarters develop a high-level design for the pilot program. They assess current spending on resources, overall plant productivity, and the overall business situation, with an eye towards determining the changes needed to meet

Exhibit 51

EXHIBIT 51

Top-down alignment and bottom-up rollout drive RPO programs

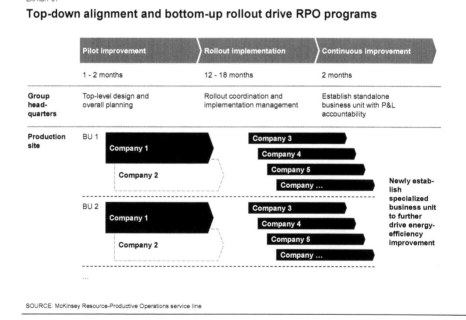

SOURCE: McKinsey Resource-Productive Operations service line

improvement targets. And they define an overall work plan. The manufacturing site chosen for the pilot evaluates its current operations to gauge its resource productivity and implements identified improvement opportunities. Furthermore, leaders consider the plant's readiness for change, including whether it has enough people, with the right skills, to make the pilot a success; what other initiatives are ongoing at the plant; and how similar the plant is to others, and thus how feasible it will be to transfer lessons learned from the pilot site to other sites.

An effective pilot program delivers important benefits. Headquarters gains an overarching conceptual design, high-level plans for driving change at other sites, and a demonstration site that can be used for best-practice sharing and capability building throughout the organization. The company also acquires a set of standardized levers for improving resource productivity. Finally, the pilot generates the first internal experts (typically called change agents) and experienced improvement leaders—as well as the first group of frontline employees. All of these individuals will be dedicated to supporting resource productivity in the organization overall and will help plant seeds for change at other sites.

Rollout

During the rollout stage, top management relies less on support from external experts and begins leveraging the change agents developed during the pilot program. Headquarters may set up a project-management office to coordinate the rollout of the new operating system and to centralize efforts aimed at building required capabilities in the organization. Such efforts may include site-level and corporatewide training sessions on resource productivity, meetings to review progress and compare it to key performance indicators (KPIs), and communications aimed at changing the organizational culture to foster awareness of the importance of assessing resource losses. The internal expert team leads the rollout of resource-productivity improvements for individual production sites, in waves.

Outcomes of these efforts include a firmly established expert team. This team can conduct an overall assessment of sites by using performance reviews of resource productivity. It will also select the appropriate resource-productivity tools to identify a comprehensive set of standardized improvement levers leading to the quantification of the resource-productivity opportunity of the sites investigated. Furthermore, the team will support the sites in the implementation phase to ensure that the desired savings are realized.

Continuous improvement

During this stage, which can start in parallel with stages 1 and 2, headquarters needs to embed a resource-productivity mind-set into the fabric of the company. A valuable step in this direction is to establish a new business unit with its own profit-and-loss responsibility and to move the internal expert team into the unit. Resource productivity and its improvement is centrally managed by the new unit. In a few cases, top management has also set up a separate company that focuses on driving implementation of all required changes on site. Other companies use more decentralized approaches involving the establishment of expert networks and the development of experts at the site level.

Outcomes of this stage include a resource-productivity governance infrastructure that can be deployed from headquarters to individual manufacturing sites; a resource-productivity management system comprising productivity targets for all resource types, scorecards, review meetings, and responsible managers; and expert subteams that can be deployed to production sites involved in subsequent waves of change.

Put simply, in a large-scale corporate transformation driven from the top down, headquarters plays a major role in working with individual manufacturing sites to spread knowledge and to bring resource-productivity capabilities and change programs to different sites (Exhibit 52).

In an organization that takes a more bottom-up approach, one might still see the three phases (pilot, rollout, and continuous improvement). But these will be applied in a less centralized way and focus on skill building at local sites, with high-level follow up and tracking provided by corporate. In one company that took this approach, the enterprise started by building the first group of experts through training at a model factory (a facility for hands-on, experiential learning),[40] followed by a see-do-teach sequence to build a core of experts. The enterprise used lessons learned from this

---

40   McKinsey Capability Center Network, http://www.capability-center.mckinsey.com/.

EXHIBIT 52

Headquarters can drive change out to individual manufacturing sites

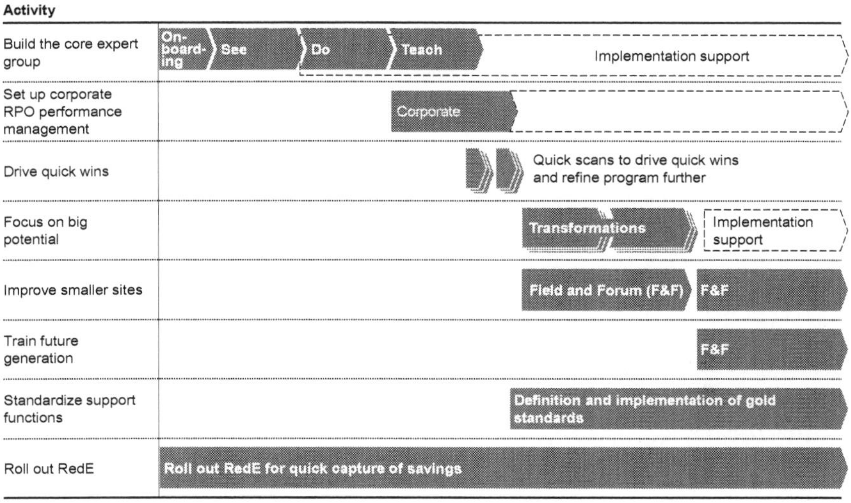

Activity

Build the core expert group	On-board-ing › See › Do › Teach ›	Implementation support
Set up corporate RPO performance management	Corporate	
Drive quick wins		Quick scans to drive quick wins and refine program further
Focus on big potential		Transformations › Implementation support
Improve smaller sites		Field and Forum (F&F) › F&F ›
Train future generation		F&F ›
Standardize support functions		Definition and implementation of gold standards ›
Roll out RedE	Roll out RedE for quick capture of savings ›

SOURCE: McKinsey Resource-Productive Operations service line

part of the process to define the performance-management system that would be developed at the corporate level to guide future continuous-improvement efforts, with an IT-tracking tool for program follow-up. Additionally, the program applied technical gold standards—equipment requirements to be met by the entire group, such as use of high-efficiency motors and quick scans to accelerate savings identification.

This was followed by short "quick scans" at key energy cost sites to front-load the program's energy savings. Once these quick scans were launched the corporate team started energy transformations or "kick starts" (deep-dive resource-productivity diagnostics) on sites with high energy and resource costs, and provided training by academies for sites with a smaller cost base. Academies used a field-and-forum approach, in which participants conducted on-the-job implementation at their workplace (the field component) and regularly convened to simultaneously provide training and identify savings opportunities (forums). Using this approach, the company could quickly build new internal capabilities across the entire organization.

Setting up the right management infrastructure

The management infrastructure needed to drive a resource-productivity change program consists of key components easily remembered as "the six Ps".

- **Process:** "Be obsessed with standards"
- **Problem solving:** "Go and see for yourself"
- **Performance:** "Be clear about your expectations"
- **Partnering:** "One team, one goal, one standard"
- **Purpose:** "Engage the hearts of your people"
- **People:** "Respect and build your teams."

Process

Process is all about being obsessed with standards. For example, everyone in the organization is focused on the customer and maintains an end-to-end perspective; that is, maximizing value-adding activities from the customer point of view. Moreover, all teams—for instance, production shifts—adhere to standard operating procedures (SOPs), setting operational parameters the same way, to the same level, such as for temperature, pressure, and flow rates. In all too many organizations, each shift tends to believe that it does things better than the others and changes parameters to what they think is best. Shifts should resist this temptation to tweak. Following standards supports efforts towards continuous improvement, because it enables people to more easily detect deviations from the standards and take action to address them, thereby relentlessly eliminating waste and ensuring the most-efficient process flows.

If SOPs haven't been reviewed in the past 12 months, this is a likely indicator that the organization is not using them—suggesting a weak management infrastructure.

Problem solving

Problem solving centers on direct observation—managers "go and see for themselves" what is happening in their company's operations. For instance, they stroll the shop floor, looking for signs of energy or material losses, such as steam or compressed air leaks, and gathering data firsthand by talking with people. Problem solving also encourages rigor and promptness in developing creative, simple, and low-cost solutions to problems observed.

Tools commonly used for problem solving include asking "why" five times to get at the root cause of a problem. To illustrate, suppose a manager walks the shop floor, talks with equipment operators, and learns of a leakage in the company's compressed air system. He might apply the "five whys" approach as follows to identify the root cause:

- **Why is the leakage occurring?** Several hoses are cracked.
- **Why are the hoses cracked?** The material they're made from is degraded.
- **Why is the material degraded?** The hoses are old.
- **Why are the hoses old?** The hoses were not checked and maintained according to the recommended service schedule.
- **Why were the hoses not checked and maintained according to the recommended service schedule?** The recommended service schedule was hard to find and was not discussed on a regular basis.

Solution: Discuss service schedules in weekly operations meetings and display on team board.

Another way to identify root causes of observed problems is to create fishbone (or Ishikawa) diagrams along the six Ms explained in Chapter 3 to articulate cause-and-effect linkages leading to a problem (Exhibit 53).

Performance

Performance focuses on achieving clarity about expectations. Leaders involved in a resource-productivity-improvement program need to define the KPIs that will show whether the program is delivering expected gains. Examples of KPIs include the following:

- Energy consumption during production and idle time
- Energy performance losses

EXHIBIT 53

This sample fishbone (Ishikawa) diagram shows several potential causes of a problem

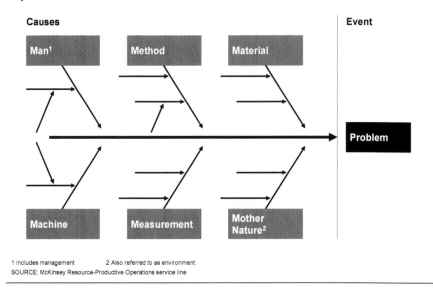

1 Includes management   2 Also referred to as environment
SOURCE: McKinsey Resource-Productive Operations service line

- Energy load losses
- Raw material cost per ton
- Number of compressed air leaks repaired out of total identified.

Adding a handful of such indicators into other KPIs that the company tracks is a simple and powerful way to focus the organization's attention on these expected areas of performance. For each KPI, leaders must also establish a target; for instance:

- Reduce energy consumption during shutdown periods to 1 MW.
- Reduce monthly energy consumption during production and idle time by 10 percent over a four-month period.

- Reduce energy performance losses by 10 percent per year.
- Reduce raw materials cost from EUR X to Y per ton over the next two years, corrected for price fluctuations in raw materials "basket."
- Move the average price of electricity consumed below the average price at constant electrical consumption.

Like other KPIs, resource-productivity performance indicators must be integrated into the organization's performance-management system with care, using demanding but achievable targets and regular performance dialogues to track progress. Organizations may also have to extend accountability for performance on such KPIs to support functions like maintenance and facilities management. The reason: these functions may have as much influence on energy consumption in a plant as the manufacturing front line has.

Leaders also need to meet regularly (daily, weekly, monthly) to compare actual performance on resource-productivity KPIs against targeted performance. Only then can they identify gaps and define actions needed to close any gaps. To illustrate, if actual monthly energy loss at a particular facility is reduced by 5 percent in the designated time frame, not the targeted 10 percent, leaders investigate the reasons behind the variance and take steps to reach the goal. Examples of steps include building "driver trees" to identify key drivers for improvement, and using the "five whys" approach to identify the root cause of the problem and to define countermeasures tailored to that cause.

Most organizations have regularly scheduled meetings to discuss key manifestations of their operational performance—such as whether operations are meeting cost, schedule, delivery, labor productivity, and quality requirements. In addition to those criteria, leaders can add resource productivity as an agenda topic for their performance-review meetings.

Partnering

When a company has a strong focus on partnering, people throughout the organization think in terms of "one team, one goal, one standard."

For any company seeking to improve its resource productivity, it will be critical for people throughout the enterprise to work together across functions. For instance, those in charge of purchasing raw materials or energy must collaborate with those in charge of production as well as those in charge of managing sales if they hope to collectively achieve the highest possible overall profit for the company. Deploying the profit-per-hour and value-in-use resource-productive-operations (RPO) methodologies is useful here. Furthermore, when it comes to equipment purchases, those in charge will need to think about total cost of owner-ship (TCO) and involve managers from the procurement, production, and maintenance teams, rather than focusing only on getting the low-est possible purchase price. Everyone involved needs to remember that operational performance in production and maintainability are just as critical.

Signs of strong partnering in an organization include a willingness and ability to "steal" ideas and copy best practices across teams and loca-tions as well as an alignment of support functions with customer-focused end-to-end processes.

In any manufacturing company, people in a wide array of functions have numerous opportunities to improve resource productivity. Thus, the leaders of a resource-productivity-improvement program should plan on involving people from all functions in identifying such opportunities and determining how best to capitalize on them. Function managers and their teams are closest to the processes and approaches that can collectively deliver productivity improvements, so they often constitute a treasure trove of good ideas. Consider:

- **Purchasing:** Resource-savvy procurement managers will take a total cost of ownership approach to buying equipment such as pumps or motors—and thus will be more likely to choose energy-efficient equipment. That's because TCO analysis will show that purchasing inefficient equipment is costly not only in terms of cash flow but also in terms of long-term spending on resources, with only 10 to 20 percent of TCO being the purchasing cost.

- **Maintenance:** Managers who have adopted a resource-productivity mindset will make repair work involving resource-related infrastructure a high priority, such as fixing compressed air pipes that are leaking or replacing insulation around steam pipes. They also know that when equipment fails or needs updating, it's better to bring in energy-efficient replacements than to merely replace an old piece of equipment with a newly manufactured version of the same design.

- **Production planning:** Such planning influences production sequence and mix, which in turn influence energy, yield, and water losses. More effective sequencing commonly helps produce the optimal batch sizes, avoiding start-up/ramp-down losses, and ensuring optimal inventory levels. Staying within certain product families that have similar specifications may avoid changeovers or clearing losses all together or can dramatically reduce the time they require. For example, planners could consider sequencing of chemical batches from higher-temperature requirements to lower ones. Reducing idling or additional cleaning requirements during equipment and product changeovers could further help reduce energy consumption. In a steel company, moving hot charge from continuous caster to hot strip mill reduced furnace energy consumption by 0.1 gigajoules per ton for each 100 degrees of average temperature increase.

- **Brownfield engineering:** Resource-smart managers in charge of these major capital upgrades—such as replacing an entire pumping system or adding new pumps—will be sure to take energy efficiency into account in their project designs. For instance, by rightsizing equipment, a company can avoid bypass and throttling losses in its pumping systems. In large industrial complexes, there is usually a wide array of pumps that frequently—for either purchase-price (volume discounts) or safety reasons—are all dimensioned the same size. Pumps as well as fans not selected for the right operating point have significant efficiency losses, and most of them run in a fixed regime (for example, with the same throughput).

- **Greenfield engineering:** Resource-minded managers of greenfield projects, such as construction of a new manufacturing site on previously uninhabited land, will resist any temptation to simply reuse old blueprints and plans developed for older projects. They know that the old approaches were likely energy inefficient. Instead, such managers view greenfield projects as excellent opportunities to avoid resource-productivity mistakes made in previous efforts. They thus take a TCO approach to develop new designs and plans aimed at capturing every possible resource-productivity opportunity. For example, installing five boiler feed-water pumps of 250 KW each instead of two pumps of 1 MW each saves capital expenditure and future operating cost while also delivering better equipment reliability.

Purpose

Purpose is about engaging the "hearts" (emotions) of people throughout the organization. A company with a clear and compelling purpose for embarking on a resource-productivity transformation journey is far more likely to win the passionate commitment of managers and employees to the effort than one with a vague or lukewarm purpose.

To communicate the purpose behind a corporate-transformation effort, companies can clarify how the organization, the individuals in it, and society will benefit if the effort succeeds. Handled skillfully, such communications ensure that all employees understand the benefits of resource productivity and know that becoming more cost competitive in a resource-constrained world is a top priority for the company.

In companies that have a strong sense of purpose, managers tell compelling stories about "what's in it" for the organization and the individuals in it if resource productivity is improved, and how this accomplishment will enable them to realize a long-term vision and achieve long-term goals. In such enterprises, employees also understand how they can make a clear, tangible contribution to those longterm objectives through their everyday, on-the-job actions.

One powerful way to strengthen people's sense of purpose is to ensure that they view their contributions to the transformation program as meaningful. Yet individuals derive a sense of meaning from five different sources. Some people feel the strongest sense of meaning in their work when they know that what they do every day is benefiting society overall. Others are focused more on how their work affects customers or the organization itself. Still others draw meaning from knowing that their everyday actions positively affect their team or their own personal and professional prospects.

Although different people gain a sense of meaning from different sources, research consistently shows that in many organizations, there will be an even distribution of 20 percent across the five sources.[41] Thus, to appeal to all employees, change leaders need to develop comprehensive stories about the benefits of change that encompass all five sources. And they must communicate these stories throughout the entire organization.

Stories that blend all five sources of meaning will prove most effective, because they will speak to everyone, especially if they end with compelling calls to action.

---

41 Keller, Scott, and Colin Price: "Beyond Performance: How Greater Organizations Build Ultimate Competitive Advantage," Hoboken, New Jersey; John Wiley & Sons, 2011.

Change leaders must make compelling calls to action to tap into employees' need for meaning

Source of meaning	Sample calls to action: "By changing how you do your work in the ways we're asking for, you'll ..."
Society	<ul><li>"Help reduce waste of scarce natural resources crucial to all forms of life on our planet"</li><li>"Help free up resources that can be channeled to people who don't have enough clean water or reliable electricity"</li><li>"Help our company sustain its operations and continue providing good jobs for thousands of employees"</li></ul>
Our company	<ul><li>"Help us reduce costs and generate new sources of revenue, which together will improve profitability"</li><li>"Enable us to attract more investment through higher profitability, which translates into more capital for us to expand our operations"</li><li>"Make our company a recognized leader in our industry"</li></ul>
Our customers	<ul><li>"Support our customers' efforts to improve resource productivity in their own operations"</li><li>"Set an inspiring example that our customers can learn from as they launch resource-productivity efforts of their own"</li><li>"Help us lower expenses so that we can make our pricing more competitive for customers"</li></ul>
Your team	<ul><li>"Help your team as a whole perform at a higher level"</li><li>"Experience the pride and satisfaction that come with being part of an exceptional team"</li><li>"Be able to share new knowledge within the team so that everyone can do their work more easily, quickly, and accurately"</li></ul>
You	<ul><li>"Build new skills that will make you more employable and qualified for possible promotion"</li><li>"Gain recognition within the company and in your field"</li><li>"Qualify for possible financial rewards, such as a bonus or stock options"</li></ul>

People

Attention to people is all about managers throughout an organization respecting and building their teams. For example, managers let the people closest to the front line make decisions about resource productivity that directly relate to their jobs. They also develop capabilities essential for improving resource productivity by providing their team members with needed training, coaching, and performance feedback. In addition, they encourage, acknowledge, and reward ideas for improving resource productivity and results achieved.

Organizations that give adequate attention to people also put the right human resources behind a transformational effort aimed at improving resource productivity. For example, in addition to the internal expert team, a company needs to put someone in charge of monitoring and managing resource productivity— such as an energy manager who will serve as the primary change agent for the resource-productivity program. This individual should report to someone at headquarters, and each manufacturing site will need at least a few people on staff who are dedicated to resource productivity.

Crafting a communication plan

The new operating system and management infrastructure that a company creates to launch a resource-productivity-improvement effort are not sufficient in themselves to ensure a successful transformation journey. Shop-floor employees throughout the organization will also have to adopt a new mind-set about resources and master new behaviors—decidedly different ways of performing their jobs. To encourage these changes, a company needs to develop a sound communication plan.

The goals of the plan include building awareness of resources among employees and helping them see the need for—and embrace—change. In particular, employees must learn which resources are used in the manufacturing operations they're involved in, what costs are associated with those resources, and how those costs compare with the value that results from the use of the resources.

A good communication plan calls for frequent and savvy use of multiple channels. For example, at town-hall-style meetings, executives can explain why a new or sharper focus on resource productivity is essential and how the company intends to improve its performance on this criterion. Articles published in the company newsletter or posted on an internal Web site devoted to the resource-productivity-improvement effort can further reinforce key messages about the program and offer tips for successfully implementing change.

Individual conversations are important reinforcement mechanisms, clarifying that what's communicated officially is supported by unofficial, word-of-mouth dialogues. Companies can also hold contests where employees submit ideas for further enhancing resource productivity in their areas of work. Those whose ideas are chosen for implementation can be recognized and rewarded in ways appropriate to the organization's culture.

The communication plan should also spell out tactics that will be deployed as the resource-productivity effort unfolds. For instance, companies can plan to put up posters in hallways, break rooms, and cafeterias that depict in accessible, graphic form the cost savings and other gains that employees help the company achieve by performing their work in new ways. Celebrating successes and sharing success stories across the organization are additional ways to keep people motivated and to share lessons learned when they encounter the inevitable setbacks during the execution of the program.

Developing required capabilities and expertise

To further prepare for a successful resource-productivity program, a company must determine how it will develop the capabilities and expertise that people will need to use new resource-productivity tools. The KPIs and targets that upper management has defined will play a major role here. For instance, if the company wants to reduce energy losses by a certain percentage in a specific time frame by implementing the RPO tools introduced in Section 2 of this book, employees will need to gain familiarity with those tools and learn how to deploy them correctly in the field.

Spotlight on storytelling

An organization's culture is communicated and reinforced through storytelling—including stories about change efforts. Stories tell employees what is and isn't acceptable, and who the heroes are in the organization. Stories thus serve as powerful learning tools. Stories about resource-productivity efforts—about failures as well as successes—can inspire employees to strive for even greater gains and warn them away from behaviors that don't support the change program. Communicated deftly, stories can drive the behaviors needed to ensure a successful transformation journey.

The best RPO change stories clearly articulate why an increase in resource productivity is required and the actions that the organization will take to achieve this aim. To get these points across, the stories relate where the company is coming from (its history with regard to resource-productivity achievements and challenges), where it is now (the "burning platform" indicating the need for change), where it wants to go (its goals, mission,

and values), and how it plans to get there. Good RPO stories also make clear who will benefit if the change program succeeds (the company overall, groups within the company, individuals, society overall), as well as how they will benefit.

Why is storytelling so powerful? The answer can be found in what's known about adult-learning theory:

- People learn and remember information that applies directly to them. When employees share stories about something that's happening in the workplace, they often share problems that other people are also grappling with. Consequently, others pay more attention to the stories and may find themselves contributing ideas for solutions. Moreover, because the information comes in the form of a story (as opposed to a lecture or words in a book), people tend to remember the information longer. The use of stories supplies information about practical application instead of just theory—creating a more effective learning experience.

- When emotions and senses are stimulated during learning, people acquire information more quickly and retain it longer. A well-told story can make people experience a wide range of emotions. Indeed, if the person telling the story has personally experienced what he or she is describing, the storyteller can't help but add emotion to the words. And listeners will respond emotionally. Good storytelling also stimulates the senses; for example, by evoking powerful imagery. This helps ensure that a story's "morale" becomes part of listeners' thinking, instead of just an external experience that drifts away once they go back to their jobs.

Source: "Storytelling—A Powerful Learning Tool," *HR.com,* last modified August 18, 2003 http://www.hr.com/ SITEFORUM?&t=/Default/gat eway&i=1116423256281&applica tion=story&acti ve=no&ParentID =1119278152254&StoryID=1119 652274843&xref=https%3A// www.google.com/; accessed July 23, 2014.

A training strategy is critical here. Training approaches may take numerous forms, including the following:

- Field-based options such as visits to model factories or production sites in other industries, as well as job shadowing
- Forum-based options including classroom learning, coaching, and mentoring workshops
- Field-and-forum-based options that use classroom learning plus selfpaced, online, IT-based coursework or three-day "boot camps" conducted before a transformation program is initiated.

Successful organizations use a combination of experiential-learning techniques and real-world experience, supported by timely coaching and mentoring, to help employees apply what they learn to their day-to-day roles. Just as employees often get their first taste of the power of lean through simple manufacturing games, staff embarking on resource-productivity-improvement programs can use a similar approach. For instance, managers can use a tabletop electroplating machine to show employees how process parameters affect energy consumption, cycle time, and quality and to help them see how they can use experimental techniques to manage the trade-offs among these criteria.

The training that a company settles on will differ depending on its situation. Consider a large cement company that makes one product. In this company, manufacturing sites are largely identical in terms of size, processes, resources and equipment used, and resource-productivity challenges. Executives conduct diagnostics across the company's main resource-productivity elements (energy, raw materials, yield losses) and identify the most prominent drivers of losses and variability. They also quantify the productivity-improvement opportunity, codify the company's new production system, and then engineer one big rollout of the system to all sites. The company will therefore likely develop a standardized training program for employees at all sites.

By contrast, at a large chemical company that produces a diverse array of products, each of its manufacturing sites may differ in many respects. This company will probably opt to develop a host of different training strategies tailored to each unique site. For instance, it may assemble a group of experts to visit each site and diagnose site-specific resource challenges as well as determine the appropriate tools to introduce into the site's production system. Training programs would likewise be customized for the selected tools and the employees at each site.

A company may also need to develop higher-level capabilities and expertise—such as advanced analytics and modeling related to assessing profit per hour, deep expertise related to specific equipment (such as boilers and compressors), and leadership skills including the ability to conduct productive performance dialogues—to support its new operating system. Some companies may choose to get outside help to develop these capabilities. For example, they may bring in content experts on a temporary basis.

However, ideally a company should eventually develop such capabilities and expertise in-house. While external content experts bring valuable knowledge to the table, companies may find it difficult to transfer that knowledge to the organization in a sustainable way. Building needed capabilities and expertise in-house encourages permanent learning and increases the likelihood of successful implementation of the change program. As Confucius put it, "I hear and I forget; I see and I remember; I do and I understand."

Moreover, in-house development can enable a company to tailor the effort to its unique circumstances. To illustrate, a cement company may need to ensure that people acquire deep expertise on just a few pieces of production equipment. By contrast, a chemical company would want people with extensive knowledge of many different types of equipment and a flexible toolbox applicable to each type of process imaginable.

Finally, in-house development of capabilities and expertise better positions a company to align the learning process with its organizational culture. In a company with a command-and-control culture, for example, skills and knowledge developed in-house through a corporate mandate can be transferred to all the company's production sites in a standardized way. In a company with a bottom-up, grassroots culture, capabilities and expertise can be built at individual sites and then be shared across sites.

Diagnosing change-management focus areas

In laying the groundwork for a successful resource-productivity transformation, companies can benefit by taking stock of three major "pieces" of such an effort— their technical system, management infrastructure, and workforce mind-sets, capabilities, and behaviors—and diagnose areas needing the most attention. They can use an online survey to do this, designing questions that focus specifically on each of these three dimensions. In diagnosing, they can look for telltale signs of problems and identify key improvement levers to focus on.

Spotlight on model factories

A learning environment and engagement tool

Model factories are experiential-learning environments that use operational shop floors, back offices, and other settings to let participants experiment with new tools and processes and experience potential improvements without worrying about risking their own operations. Such factories can serve as effective training forums for quickly building the skills and knowledge at scale that are needed to enhance resource productivity in a company's manufacturing operations.

But model factories can also be a powerful means for engaging workers in a resource-productivity change program. They help people see what's possible—triggering widespread conviction that a company can indeed reach a much higher level of performance in its use of resources. The momentum that such a factory creates can be crucial for changing the attitudes, capabilities, and behaviors of thousands of employees who are using hundreds of processes and systems at locations around the world.

An honest picture of operations

In addition to teaching necessary capabilities and engaging employees, model factories provide an environment that lets participants understand the current state of their processes and systems (no matter how sub-optimal), envision an aspirational future state, and see a path between the two. Learners start by mastering some basic tools for improving shop-floor operations and then gradually work with more advanced tools. They quickly grasp the full potential for improvements, and test their ideas in the model factory.

For example, at a model factory in Singapore that focuses on energy efficiency, learning efforts center on several subsystems commonly seen in a continuous-process industry, such as air compressors, furnaces, cooling-water systems, distillation, and heat exchanges. The current state reflects conditions found in many factories. For instance, air intake to the furnace is excessive, causing the company to waste fuel by heating air unnecessarily.

And there's a mismatch between cooling-water capacity and cooling-water needs.

Participants learn basic tools for identifying and estimating losses typical of these and other inefficiencies. Armed with these new capabilities, they walk through the factory, monitor the various controls, and locate efficiency-improvement opportunities. Next, working with coaches, they design an improved state for the factory and calculate improvement potential. Most are amazed by their transformation program's value when they see that simple tools learned reasonably quickly can capture savings of 10 to 30 percent of factory operating costs—and in some cases more.

But model factories are more than just technical, shop-floor environments. They also mirror a real factory environment and have equipment operators who role-play mind-sets, capabilities, and behaviors typically displayed by the front line in participants' own facilities. These operators can at times drive the most learning in participants. They get a chance to experience what it takes to make change happen and stick long term.

An antidote to resistance

Model factories can erode resistance to change from skeptics or workers who have been in their roles for many years and aren't convinced that change is needed or worry that change will put their jobs in jeopardy. By taking them out of their daily environments, the factories remove these stakeholders from their habits and help them to be more open to experimenting with new ideas.

The risk-free setting lets them explore how change can lead to improvements and to apply new tools and capabilities without fear that success might reflect badly on their own work. As a result, they may be more eager to bring their new capabilities back to their own workplaces, where their conviction can spread quickly among their colleagues. They thus become powerful agents of change.

Source:
Lauritzen, Mads D., Martin Joerss, and Foo Leong Wong: "Chapter 3: Model factories create conviction and confidence," in *Capability for performance: The path to excellence*, McKinsey & Company, May 2012.

Diagnosing problems helps companies focus their RPO efforts

Change effort "piece"	Examples of symptoms to watch for	Potential improvement levers
Technical system	▪ Limited transparency of resource-productivity data ▪ Disconnection between resource-saving technology and operations ▪ Daily operations management that doesn't take resource productivity into account	▪ Enrich and standardize resource-productivity tool sets
Management infrastructure	▪ Scattered functional siloes with inconsistent and unaligned KPIs ▪ Insufficient breakdown of KPIs into leading, lagging, and leveling ▪ No resource-productivity performance dialogue or performance system ▪ No incentives aimed at encouraging resource productivity ▪ No emphasis on TCO approach	▪ Establish a resource-productivity project-management office ▪ Reshape headquarters-to-site resource-productivity-governance infrastructure
Mind-sets, capabilities, and behaviors	▪ Lack of awareness or understanding of resource productivity ▪ Limited understanding of why resource productivity requires management, what to manage differently, and how to do so ▪ Unwillingness to integrate resource-productivity programs into operations ▪ Shortage of resource-productivity expertise	▪ Build up needed capabilities and foster the right mind-sets and behaviors

✷✷✷

Executing a resource-productivity-transformation program is no small feat. To boost the chances of success, companies need to lay a solid foundation before launching such a program. By mastering key prerequisites, manufacturers can more effectively optimize operations at one or more of their production sites for maximum resource productivity. Forward-thinking companies not only set the stage for making the right modifications to their operating system, they also establish the right management

A case in point: Boosting energy efficiency at a Chinese materials group

Many companies in a large, state-owned basic-materials manufacturing group headquartered in China were struggling with profit losses stemming from rising raw material prices alongside a significant drop in finished-goods prices. From 2007 through 2012, the group saw its net margins plummet from 15.2 percent to a negative 5.8 percent.

In 2012, headquarters decided to launch an energy-efficiency improvement program, and it set up a project-management office (PMO) to drive the effort. The PMO, which was part of headquarters and reported to it, diagnosed energy consumption within the group's companies. It aimed to conduct pilot programs at the best-performing plants and ultimately to roll out the transformation program to eight alumina companies, with an annualized cost-reduction potential of RMB 2 billion, and to 14 electrolytic aluminum companies, with an annualized cost-reduction potential of RMB 1 billion. Total potential energy-cost savings added up to RMB 3 billion, of which RMB 1.4 billion were captured by the end of 2013.

A successful pilot program

The group conducted a pilot change program in one alumina company. To support this effort, the PMO aligned the company's functions behind the pilot program by telling the change story—including laying out the objectives of the program, celebrating the success of the pilot, explaining the resources required, and explaining what forms of support would be provided. Headquarters also leveraged model sites to begin building expertise in energy efficiency based on production needs and utility types. In addition, it benchmarked the company's energy consumption performance against national standards and specialized power-plant management practices. To improve energy efficiency at the company, the pilot concentrated on improving end-to-end management of operations (coal to gas, gas burning, coal to steam, and steam usage). Additional ideas included coal mixing for better performance, increasing sourcing choices by adding negotiation power, and eventually moving to a centralized coal-sourcing strategy.

Moreover, the pilot-site CEO led a few key projects and set up a dedicated award category on the shift and shop-floor levels to encourage energy-management awareness among frontline employees and to motivate them to support the changes. He also established strict control over key processes such as coal-quality checking, key burning parameters control, and steam supply-and-demand balancing. And he cascaded energy-related KPIs (such as calories and water percentage in coal, oxygen level, water blowdown, and burning temperature) down to individual shifts at the company.

In 2012 alone, the pilot company achieved annualized energy-cost savings of RMB 210 million and pocketed additional income of RMB 100 million. Total potential energy-cost savings added up to RMB 3 billion, of which 1.4 billion RMB in cash savings were realized in 2013.

Rollout and results

To support adoption of the new technical system developed and tested through the pilot program, the group rolled out the system to the rest of the selected alumina companies and the 14 selected electrolytic aluminum companies in early 2013. A corporate Energy Excellence SWAT Team was set up as part of the new management infrastructure and charged with conducting trial runs of the new operating system at the different companies as well as visiting the sites on a quarterly basis to provide support. The China Center for Operations Excellence provided training for the selected companies. Additional reinforcement of the required mind-set and behaviors came from train-the-trainer programs and full-time energy-efficiency leaders who helped drive implementation of the change programs at each company.

By the end of 2013, the eight alumina sites had achieved energy cost savings of about RMB 807 million. The 14 electrolytic aluminum companies achieved savings of RMB 403.6 million.

To put such gains into context, we calculated that if these gains were achieved at 35 additional global energy and materials state-owned enterprises in China, the savings would amount to as much as 1 percent of China's gross domestic product—something to think about indeed.

infrastructure and deploy mechanisms aimed at encouraging the right mind-set and behaviors throughout their workforce.

Investing time and effort upfront in these imperatives may seem frustrating for operations executives eager to move swiftly to capture the resource-productivity prize. But the investment will enable them to more effectively launch site-specific optimization programs (discussed in Chapter 9). It will also pay big dividends in the form of sustainable, long-term increases in resource yield and cost—gains that continue to burnish companies' bottom line.

CHAPTER 9

OPTIMIZING YOUR MANUFACTURING SITE

*M*anufacturers seeking to optimize operations at one or more production sites to improve resource productivity can get an excellent head start by mastering the key prerequisites described in Chapter 8. They can further raise the odds of a successful transformation program by approaching site optimization as a disciplined process comprising four steps: (1) prepare, (2) diagnose, (3) design and plan, and (4) implement and sustain. This process unfolds over the three dimensions discussed in Chapter 6 (technical systems, management infrastructure, and mindsets, capabilities, and behaviors) using the tools learned in Chapters 3 through 6. Each step will generate specific key outcomes and entail different activities centered on each of the dimensions.

Meet John: Change agent in charge

As is the case with any large-scale transformation program, optimizing a manufacturing site calls for savvy change management. The four-step, three-dimension framework described in this chapter isn't new; it contains elements based on a broad change-management philosophy. However, we have geared it to the unique characteristics of resource-productivity-improvement journeys. We identify the tools from McKinsey's proprietary tool kit that may best be deployed during each stage in the transformation process. And we offer several recommendations for further enhancing the odds of successful, sustainable change.

To put a human face on the story, we introduce you to John, a fictionalized resource-productivity change agent charged with optimizing one of a large chemical company's 150 manufacturing sites. John's company is headquartered in Europe. The site slated for optimization has an annual energy bill of roughly EUR 10 million and an annual raw materials bill of about EUR 50 million. Throughout the chapter, we show you the kinds of actions John might take during each of the four steps in the process and the results he might get. We also provide several "case in point" examples to further illustrate what site optimization looks like in action.

A closer look at the three transformation dimensions

As a resource-productivity transformation unfolds, individuals in charge of each of the three transformation dimensions will focus their efforts on specific activities. For instance, during the change journey, those orchestrating changes to the technical system (manufacturing operations, processes, and production setups and sequences of events) are typically change agents working with process engineers and production managers. They will primarily be involved in diagnosing resource losses throughout the system, identifying and quantifying improvement levers, and designing the system's desired future state.

Individuals leading changes related to management infrastructure—generally site managers along with the change agents, process engineers, and production managers—will concentrate on defining the right resource-productivity KPIs, setting targets for those KPIs, monitoring progress and resolving issues, and sustaining gains through ongoing, rigorous performance reviews and dialogue.

Meanwhile, all of these same individuals will also play a role in fostering the mindset, capabilities, and behaviors critical for supporting desired changes to the company's way of operating—with guidance from the human resources department; health, safety, and environment personnel; and communications experts. Together, they will channel their energies towards communicating the need for change, infusing a

EXHIBIT 54

Optimizing a manufacturing site entails a four-step process

① Prepare	② Diagnose	③ Design and plan	④ Implement and sustain
What is the current state?	Where are the resource losses and improvement levers?	What is the transformation design?	How is the transformation sustained?

	① Prepare	② Diagnose	③ Design and plan	④ Implement and sustain
Activities	• Understand the need for change • Define the baseline • Build conditions for success	• Perform comprehensive diagnostic • Identify improvement levers	• Set the target for the future state design • Set deployment agenda and mobilize the site for implementation	• Launch implementation plan • Set up continuous improvement mechanisms to sustain impact
Typical timing[1]	1 - 2 months before kickoff	1 - 3 months	1 - 3 weeks	3 - 12 months or more

1 Timing of each step depends on transformation characteristics such as size of plant and scope of transformation
SOURCE: McKinsey Resource-Productive Operations service line

continuous-improvement mind-set into the organization, and providing training that encourages the right behaviors among employees.

In the sections that follow, we examine more closely what happens in each of these three dimensions during every step in the change journey: prepare, diagnose, design and plan, and implement and sustain (Exhibit 54).

Step 1: Prepare

The prepare step is all about building a baseline for the transformation process. Handled deftly, it enables executives and managers to assess the current state of the site's technical system, management infrastructure, and mind-set and behaviors. This step entails the collection of large volumes of data, which can then be used to diagnose problem areas needing resolution and to develop an action plan for change.

With these imperatives in mind, our protagonist, John, starts things off by administering an online survey to the site's management team. The survey contains questions about the technical system such as "How do you purchase energy/ utilities?", "How do you manage the way energy is transported across your facility?", and "What are your current energy consumption practices?" Questions related to management infrastructure include "How do you set targets for energy and yield?", "How do you design energy and materials key performance indicators (KPIs)?", and "To what extent is resource productivity included in your performance-review process?" Questions related to mind-set, capabilities, and behaviors include "How do you foster awareness of resource productivity?", "How do you build skills and capabilities needed to increase resource productivity?", and "In what respects do leaders serve as role models supporting resource-productivity initiatives?"

In addition to the online survey, John uses several resource-productive operations (RPO) tools to gather more data on each of the three dimensions of the site, while also getting a first rough overview of the site utility and production units.

John's site has numerous utility and production units

Boiler house   Batch reactor department

Cooling towers

Dryer department

Technical system

Preparation efforts related to the technical system include assessing costs, the state of equipment, production mix, and so forth. To this end, John works with process engineers and production managers at the site to establish a baseline for the site's resource consumption and costs. He makes use of several RPO tools:

- **Utility matrix:** To establish a detailed financial baseline and to allocate energy costs over three categories: purchased, transformed, and consumed
- **Yield theoretical limit:** Used at the stoichiometric level to determine value lost from raw materials and to assess the value at stake at the plant
- **Waste walk:** To quickly address the state of the asset, the mindset of the people working there, and the current approach to resource-performance management
- **Value-at-stake analysis:** To identify the resource impact of a 1 percent change in yield and throughput.

John submits requests to the site manager for data required for the utility matrix and yield theoretical limit. The site manager, in turn, works with his team (including the site's finance and accounting manager, production and engineering managers, process engineers, and equipment operators) to fill out a data-request template that John will use in in the diagnose phase).

John agrees with the site manager to do a waste walk, during which he plans to follow the production process and look into the utility areas, with specific attention to the control rooms. In each area, he intends to talk with the respective operators and supervisors to understand the process in detail. He also arranges to meet the process engineers to discuss the value at stake if 1 percent yield or throughput could be gained at the site.

John's findings

Through use of the utility matrix and online survey, John discovers that the site employees aren't aware of how much certain utilities are costing the site. For instance, when he tells them that the cost of electricity used to provide cooling water to the chemical-production process accounts for as much as one-third of the site's total electricity consumption, they express astonishment. He also learns that steam, which is used to heat the product, is a larger than expected part of the site's cost base. Steam is consumed mainly in two process steps with condensate return from the batch reactor department only, as indicated by the mass balance John built as part of the utility-matrix effort. Furthermore, people at the site had not been aware of how the penalties for peak load and power factor into the current contracts with utilities.

In addition, John finds that they've been underestimating raw materials yield. For example, they had been (proudly) claiming a yield of 1.2 kilograms in raw material for every kilogram of product sold. But when John compares mass in versus mass out on a dry basis and corrects for additives, the theoretical yield turns out to be 1.4 kilograms of raw material for every kilogram of product sold.

He also learns that the site is not running at full production capacity and needs to close down one day a week, and that a 1 percent gain in throughput has a limited value. He also learns that a 1 percent material yield improvement would result in almost a 0.5 percent margin improvement.

During his waste walk, John had talked with a number of equipment operators about their work and what they considered their main responsibilities. An operator of a piece of equipment that required immense quantities of heat cited "safety, good quality throughput, and no process hiccups" as the parameters he paid the most attention to. He made no mention of heat consumption.

Management infrastructure

On the management-infrastructure front, preparation efforts center on understanding what's already in place within the organization to support site transformation—such as past projects; current training resources; clear accountability for energy, yield, and water use within the organization; current KPIs for measuring resource-productivity performance; and obvious management oversight of resource productivity.

John includes attention to such aspects of management infrastructure in his waste walk. For instance, he finds out which energy and yield KPIs are already in use at the site and considers whether they are specific enough—and whether the site has a sufficient number of such KPIs.

John's findings

Through a combination of the waste walk and the responses to the online survey that he sent out, John learns that the site has defined KPIs for yield but not for energy. Moreover, the yield KPIs have vague definitions. In addition, site leaders have not defined who is accountable for performance on each KPI, and resource productivity is not discussed during performance reviews conducted for site managers and employees.

Mind-sets, capabilities, and behaviors

To assess current mind-sets, capabilities, and behaviors among leaders and employees at the site, John interviews the management team to see how they would characterize the site's organizational culture and capabilities. He also administers another survey—this one to the entire workforce—to gauge current views of resource productivity at the site.

John's findings

By analyzing the responses from his interviews with the management team, his survey of workers at the site, and his initial overall online survey, John concludes that few employees know about resource-productivity-improvement initiatives that the site had launched in the past. Moreover, executives and employees alike acknowledge spotty communication within the site about why resource productivity is important or what the site plans to do about it. Employees have never been offered formalized training on resource management, and they don't know of any in-house experts on resource productivity who are active at the site or even who have a discernible presence.

Drawing on insights gained during the prepare phase, John now drafts a diagnostic schedule that focuses on the high-priority opportunity areas. In drafting this schedule, he determines what diagnostic work needs to be done, when, and by whom.

John uses a data-request template like this one

Purchased costs and sales value							
Total					Fixed		
EUR millions					EUR millions		
		2011	2012	2013	2011	2012	2013
Raw materials	Material 1	0	0	0			
	Material 2	0	0	0			
	Material 3	0	0	0			
	Material 4	0	0	0			
Sales	Product 1	0	0	0			
	Product 2	0	0	0			
Consumables	Consumable 1	0	0	0			
	Consumable 2	0	0	0			
	Consumable 3	0	0	0			
	Consumable 4	0	0	0			
Disposal cost Incl. handling	Solid 1	0	0	0			
	Solid 2	0	0	0			
	Liquid 1	0	0	0			
	Liquid 2	0	0	0			
By-product sales Incl. handling	By-product 1	0	0	0			
	By-product 2	0	0	0			
	By-product 3	0	0	0			
	By-product 4	0	0	0			
Transformed utility from utility matrix	Electricity— including produced	0	0	0			
	Natural gas	0	0	0			
	Steam—P1 bar	0	0	0			
	Steam—P2 bar	0	0	0			
	Steam—P3 bar	0	0	0			
	Steam—P4 bar	0	0	0			
	Hot water—X °C	0	0	0			
	Indust. water	0	0	0			
	Potable water	0	0	0			
	Waste water	0	0	0			
	Demin water	0	0	0			
	Compressed air	0	0				
	Cooling water	0	0	0			
Total		0	0	0	0	0	0

Variable			Price				Consumed/sold volume			
EUR millions										
2011	2012	2013	EUR/Unit	2011	2012	2013	Unit	2011	2012	2013
0	0	0	EUR/ton				ton			
0	0	0	EUR/ton				ton			
0	0	0	EUR/ton				ton			
0	0	0	EUR/ton				ton			
0	0	0	EUR/ton				ton			
0	0	0	EUR/ton				ton			
0	0	0	EUR/ton				ton			
0	0	0	EUR/ton				ton			
0	0	0	EUR/ton				ton			
0	0	0	EUR/ton				ton			
0	0	0	EUR/ton				ton			
0	0	0	EUR/ton				ton			
0	0	0	EUR/ton				ton			
0	0	0	EUR/ton				ton			
0	0	0	EUR/ton				ton			
0	0	0	EUR/ton				ton			
0	0	0	EUR/ton				ton			
0	0	0	EUR/ton				ton			
0	0	0	EUR/mwh							
0	0	0	EUR/GJ							
0	0	0	EUR/ton							
0	0	0	EUR/ton							
0	0	0	EUR/ton							
0	0	0	EUR/ton							
0	0	0	EUR/1,000 m³							
0	0	0	EUR/1,000 m³							
0	0	0	EUR/1,000 m³							
0	0	0	EUR/1,000 m³							
0	0	0	EUR/1,000 Nm³							
0	0	0	EUR/MWh							
0	0	0								

A diagnostic resource plan focuses on high-priority opportunities

Area	Analysis	Data acquisition time	Data acquirer
	Utility matrix	1.0	Controller
	Contracts	0.3	Controller
	Heat cost curve	0.3	Controller
	T,Q quick pinch map	0.3	Maintenance operator
	Transformer load	0.3	Maintenance operator
	Steam network map	0.5	Utility engineer
	Steam mass balance	0.5	Utility engineer
	Steam energy balance	0.5	Utility engineer
	Steam grid maintenance practice check	0.5	Maintenance manager
	Boiler theoretical limit	0.5	Maintenance operator
	Boiler room electrical user theoretical limit		Combined
	Fermenter compressor Technical map	0.5	Maintenance operator
	Fermenter compressor load curve		Combined
	Fermenter compressor air pressure drop TL(JV with fermentation)	1.0	Production engineer fermentation
Utilities	Cooling water—pump TL	0.3	Maintenance operator
	Fermenter compressor—flow, temperature, pressure, height, control mapping	1.5	All production engineers + operator
	Cooling water—required pressure TL		Combined
	Cooling water—temp over time, vs. flow over time using LMTD for key users		Combined
	Instrument air technical map	n/a	n/a
	Instrument air maintenance practices	n/a	n/a
	RedE setup	n/a	n/a
	Very cold media—technical map	n/a	n/a
	Idea generation and prioritization and quantification	n/a	n/a
	Idea evaluation	n/a	n/a
	Planning and presentation building	n/a	n/a

Assume two change agents full time (four days per week on site)

Change agent time	Week												
	1	2	3	4	5	6	7	8	9	10	11	12	13
	Diagnose						Idea generation			Idea evaluation			Idea planning
2.0	1.0												
1.0	1.0												
1.0	1.0												
1.0		1.0											
0.5													
1.0		1.0											
0.5		1.0											
0.5		1.0											
0.5			1.0										
0.5			1.0										
0.5			1.0										
0.5					1.0								
0.5					1.0								
1.5					1.0								
0.5				1.0									
2.0				1.0									
0.5				1.0									
0.5				1.0									
tbc													
tbc													
1.0	0.2	0.2	0.2	0.2	0.2								
tbc													
4.0							0.5	0.5					
7.0										0.3	0.3	0.3	
2.0													1.0

187

Step 2: Diagnose

The diagnose step centers on identifying resource losses stemming from the site's current operations and defining improvement levers. This step constitutes the major work required in the site-optimization process. John must draw on his interpretations of the extensive data he gathered during the prepare stage as well as additional efforts to prioritize the problems that require attention regarding the site's technical system, management infrastructure, and mind-set, capabilities, and behaviors.

Technical system

John has defined the theoretical limit of consumption of resources such as energy, materials, and water at the site and has quantified the potential impact; that is, the difference between the site's current cost situation and the suggested improved state, or theoretical limit. Take steam and cooling water, for example. He has discovered that steam constitutes a large portion of the site's current cost base and that steam still has a substantial gap compared to the theoretical limit. Given that cooling water is one-third of the electrical cost base, John decides to investigate this further, using the following RPO tools:

- **Technical map**: To discover key technical parameters and system control logic (boiler house, cooling water, batch reactor department, and dryer department)
- **Cost curve**: To quantify losses due to resource demand-supply mismatch (boiler house)
- **Network map**: To map and quantify losses in makeup distribution networks (steam and cooling water)
- **Loss bridge**: To identify the minimum theoretical level of resource consumption (batch reactor department, dryer, and cooling water pumps)
- **Load curve**: To quantify performance losses on equipment/process/production over time and versus production speed (dryer and batch reactor department)
- **Shutdown analyses**: To identify energy consumption during idle times (overall site)

- **Machine system analyses**: To prioritize motors, pumps, and fans for loss quantification due to inefficiencies (cooling water pumps)
- **Quick pinch**: To quantify losses due to suboptimal reuse of heat (batch reactor department).

John starts with the site electricity load curve, focusing on the site's consumption over time to better understand the peak penalties currently being paid. He speaks with managers in the main departments to identify the source of the demand peaks.

After learning more about the contractual losses, he continues with energy makeup and transportation. For instance, he builds a technical map of the site's boiler house indicating stack gas temperatures, excess oxygen percentages, boiler capacities, boiler utilization, condensate return, condensate return temperature, and other data.

He also uses cost curve analysis for the site's three boilers, indicating boiler-capacity utilization and operation cost, including steam-demand patterns. Next, he focuses on the transportation of steam in the site—by building a network map showing all makeup and consumption points, network pressures, and mass flows. In addition, he performs a machine-system analysis on the cooling-water system (pumps and fans) and builds a network map indicating flows and temperature differentials.

John also continues to investigate the energy consumers. To understand the gaps among the actual consumption, best demonstrated practice, and theoretical limit, he builds loss bridges for the batch reactor and dryer department, covering the majority of the utility cost base. As part of this effort, he also builds technical maps, load curves, and shutdown analyses.

John finalizes his investigation to look for integration options. In addition, he conducts a quick-pinch analysis of how the product flows through the process and indicates temperature and the active use of heat and cold at each stage.

John's diagnoses

John's deep dive into the site's electricity-demand peaks reveals the reactor department as the main reason for the largest peaks and, more specifically, the peaks that occur on Monday morning when the facility starts up again after the Sunday shutdown. His interviews with operators suggest that the three main stirred reactors are always started in parallel; thus, they are the most likely source of the large demand peaks.

After reviewing his technical map of the site's boiler house, John finds that the exhaust gas temperature of boiler 1 is at 180 degrees, because the economizer is worn out and is now bypassed. The oxygen percentage of all stacks is above 5 percent, and the boiler feed-water pumps are working against a 50 percent closed valve. Not all condensate is returned, and the temperature in the condensate return vessel is only 70 degrees. John plans to use these points in further discussions to identify the drivers behind these first findings.

From his cost curve analysis, he concludes that the load is evenly spread across the three boilers at 50 percent load. One out of the three is substantially less efficient. Only 2 percent of all times, this third inefficient boiler is required. Analysis of the high steam-demand times points to a joint start of batch reactor heating as the main culprit. Changing programming practices could make the third boiler obsolete or place it in permanent pressurized hot standby—depending on value-at-risk analysis of a boiler trip.

John's network map indicates a pressure drop from 20 to 5 bars when entering the dryer department, as only low temperature is required to dry the product. This department is also the main one responsible for lack of condensate return.

The cooling system analysis shows a performant cooling-water pump system with pump-motor efficiency of approximately 80 percent and limited pressure and flow losses in the system. The temperature of the cooling water entering the cooling towers is 10 degrees below design, and the temperature differential is only 4 degrees. Further probing at the consumer side reveals the use of bypasses to control the temperature profile in the batch reactors, leading to excessive flow and small temperature differentials. The cooling-water temperature was lowered in the past to drive faster cooling and gain production speed—a practice that makes less sense during the current market downturn.

The batch-reactor loss bridge shows large shutdown losses and large fixed steam consumption. The main drivers are the weekend cleaning practices and the lack of insulation and presence of steam leaks at the reactors and their respective piping. The dryer loss bridge shows a large performance loss linked to variability in incoming moisture content and exit temperature. Both shutdown and load losses are smaller in nature.

John's quick-pinch analysis shows that the chemical process in the reactor department involves bringing the materials from room temperature to 170 degrees and then cooling to 40 degrees for storage, for multiple steps. He believes that this is an opportunity for heat integration or heat-profile flattening, to help the site avoid spending too much money to heat and cool the product.

John also looks into yield losses, using the following RPO tools:

- **Resource value stream map (Sankey diagram)**: To identify main areas in process flow where value is being lost owing to yield losses
- **Yield loss bridge**: To map yield loss sources within a specific process step
- **Yield-driver tree**: To list driving parameters behind yield losses in a specific process step
- **Process-parameter analyses**: To identify and quantify the most relevant process parameters driving yield in the process step under investigation.

John builds a resource value stream map for the main cost-driving product group and identifies the third step in the reactor process as the yield loss driving most of the value loss. He takes a closer look at that third reactor process step and builds a loss bridge splitting operational and design losses.

To better understand the losses, he creates a yield-driver tree with input from operators, process engineers, corporate specialists, and a literature research. He uses the historical batch record data as a design-of-experiment set and performs process-parameter analysis on this data set to strengthen his understanding of the yield-driving parameters.

John's diagnoses

John's value stream map shows large losses in the first reaction step, but with a product of limited cost. The most valuable products are being added in the second reaction step, but with very limited yield losses. The third reaction step, though, has moderate yield losses and thereby destroys the value added in the second step. The fourth step is the bottleneck reaction, but given the low market demand, little value is added there.

John's loss bridge for the third reaction step shows load and performance losses as operational losses, suggesting a time dependence in the reaction and variability in input or controlling parameters. The design part of the loss bridge shows physical losses in the emptying of the reactor and chemical losses in the unreacted excess reagent and by-product formed.

John builds driver trees for the chemical loss buckets, investigating parameters such as reaction duration, excess reagent, pressure, temperature, stirring speed, and addition timing. He does this for all reactions involved, including by-product reactions.

Using advanced analytics techniques, he identifies the intricate interplays among reaction duration, temperature, and excess reagent. He uses his understanding of these relationships to build a model that shows the optimal parameters given product cost and margin as input parameters. Second-order parameters are the speed of heating and pressure in the vessel.

In parallel, John had assessed the overall profit per hour, using several of the RPO tools:

- **Historical profit-per-hour curve and best demonstrated practice:** To understand value at stake through overall profit optimization and to get a better sense of the size of interactions
- **Sales and margin analyses based on profit per hour:** To assess whether the site's current product portfolio maximizes value.

John wants to get an overall view of the site's profitability and interactions and assesses the site's profit per hour using historical cost and price data. The data suggest that product mix is a key driver, so John launches a sales and margin analysis based on profit per hour.

John's diagnoses

The historical profit-per-hour data show large peaks and troughs that cannot be explained by cost (yield and energy) variability. Deeper investigation reveals that the site's product mix has a large impact on its profitability, with some days showing very limited profit.

By analyzing sales and margin using profit per hour instead of profit per ton, John identifies two product groups that have high value per ton but long production times; they thus have low profit per hour. The identified profit-per-hour margins for these products suggest that they are below fixed cost per hour. John decides that continuation of these products needs to be investigated, because the site could potentially close down for an additional day to increase overall margin.

Management infrastructure

The work on the technical system has helped John build a better understanding of the critical parameters and trade-offs for both energy and yield. He uses this knowledge to help the site define new energy and yield KPIs. He has also observed shift handover meetings as well as daily management and weekly management meetings.

Additionally, he conducts a structured interview with the site manager and production head to gain insights into the site's performance-management system. During the interview, he refers to survey questions and responses that he sees as particularly troubling. He uses open-ended questions to get his interviewees' thoughts on how the site could improve its score on those questions. For instance, he says, "In selecting the number that most closely describes the site's resource-productivity KPI design practices, the overriding response was 1 on a scale of 1 to 5. What changes would we need to make in order to get an overriding response of 5 if we took the survey again?"

John's diagnoses

In John's view, the problems he found with the site's KPIs merit serious attention. He knows that the site needs to add energy KPIs and refine its yield KPIs. Examples include splitting energy KPIs into production and shutdown losses, cascading leading and lagging KPIs for both energy and yield, and defining a yield optimizer model to help managers determine how best to schedule shifts to maximize margins. Moreover, the KPIs that the site has established are tracked at the day level. John believes that they should be extended to the shift level, because of the important role the operators can play in improving energy efficiency and yield. In addition, John believes that the fact that resource productivity is not being discussed routinely during performance reviews and other meetings at the site (such as shift handovers as well as daily and weekly management meetings) constitutes another major concern.

Mind-set, capabilities, and behaviors

John uses the online survey results he gathered during the prepare phase, comments made during his observations of the work on site, and insights gathered from his management-infrastructure work to conduct detailed, face-to-face interviews with a handful of key individuals at the site, including the energy manager and shop-floor managers. During the interviews, he tries to get a sense of their mind-set vis-a-vis resource productivity and what they see as their main responsibilities. Additionally, he assesses the capabilities present at the operator and management levels on the subject of resource productivity.

John's diagnoses

These conversations confirm what John suspected when he analyzed the online survey results from the prepare phase: lack of awareness of resource productivity and training on the subject are serious shortcomings for the site. For instance, managers and workers aren't aware of energy's cost implications and don't think about translating consumption of energy into euros. If they were able to make this translation, John knows that they'd be better motivated to find ways to control costs—such as repairing steam leaks more quickly. He also believes that managers must make better use of multiple communication channels to raise awareness of resource productivity and of the site's current performance on its energy and yield KPIs. And he pronounces the site's current training programs woefully inadequate.

Having diagnosed problem areas, John is ready to move forward to the design and plan stage.

Step 3: Design and plan

In the design and plan stage, John determines what the site-optimization rollout will look like in action—by identifying improvement initiatives for its technical system, management infrastructure, and mind-set, capabilities, and behaviors.

Technical system

John consolidates technical-system initiatives and builds a database of improvement initiatives that includes information such as initiative names, persons responsible for leading each initiative, potential improvements, descriptions of the opportunity, capital-expenditure requirements, and payback period. He also decides to make use of the RedE online tool to manage and track progress on each initiative.

He then translates the initiatives into action plans and documents them in the master plan, which shows how the initiatives are sequenced and how resources will be allocated to each. Because the

A case in point: Diagnosing needed change at a fertilizer company

In 2007, a fertilizer company conducted a diagnosis of its resource-productivity performance. The diagnosis revealed that energy represented about 15 percent of the company's cost base. Executives set improvement goals including transforming the company from an energy consumer to an energy producer by 2013. They identified a number of improvement levers that they believed would help them achieve this goal. Such levers included enhancing energy efficiency by introducing an energy-performance-management system and making small capital upgrades (such as steam-pipe-line repair). They also created a new energy-manager position to sustain resource-productivity gains that

they hoped the change program would produce. And they set a goal of making larger capital investments later to support the transformation from energy consumer to energy producer.

The global economic crisis delayed the implementation of those later capital investments. However, the company managed to reduce its energy costs by a whopping 77 percent within just two years of the diagnosis, largely by optimizing its energy consumption through changes such as improved maintenance procedures. The larger capital-investment projects still in the pipeline are expected to capture more energy from the lower-temperature range of the exothermic reactions in the company's plant operations.

initiatives can't all be implemented simultaneously, the plan depicts how resources will be channeled towards the projects with the highest impact first. In the master plan, initiatives that are especially complex are accompanied by more detailed tactical implementation plans.

John's initiatives

John's master plan includes numerous initiatives related to improving the site's technical system. Here are just a few examples:

- Install model to optimize yield as function of throughput, product cost, and margin.
- Control moisture levels in products that are being dried so that energy consumption required for drying is decreased. Because water levels depend on the filtering process in the reactor department, performance management on this parameter at the reactor department will be critical.
- Improve temperature control at the dryer to avoid overheating and wasting heating energy.
- Return condensate from the dryer to the boiler house, and insulate overall condensate return grid.
- Define a standard operating procedure for the reactor optimizer model, taking into account raw material cost and sales margins.
- Improve insulation at the reactor department to drive down fixed consumption.
- Avoid heating and cooling in reactor department for one heat-insensitive step, and investigate hot-water-system introduction.
- Install shutdown practices for the reactor department to reduce Sunday costs.
- Install backpressure turbine to replace 20-to-5-bar pressure-reducing valve in steam grid.
- Run with two boilers, and install steam-peak management system.
- Install reactor startup practices to avoid electricity-peak penalty.
- Ensure that boiler-maintenance company places the excess oxygen percentage at 3 percent at 75 to 100 percent load.

Management infrastructure

Using the outcomes from the previous phases, John designs and plans activities related to management infrastructure. These activities focus on KPIs and training.

John's initiatives

Initiatives related to management infrastructure in John's master plan include:

- Define a better set of resource-productivity KPIs (including energy metrics).
- Cascade the KPIs to the line level.
- Establish a disciplined schedule of meetings to review progress on those KPIs.
- Create a program to develop new capabilities that employees will need to support changes made to the site's technical system.
- Provide training to teach site executives and managers how to conduct effective dialogues on the site's resource-productivity performance.
- Create a new part-time role—energy consumption manager— because the utility manager currently focuses on energy provision but not reduction of energy consumption. Have the new energy consumption manager begin reviewing energy consumption numbers with the plant manager, utility manager, and production and engineering managers on a regular basis to brainstorm ideas for reducing consumption. (Because the site—like many manufacturing facilities—lacks sufficient engineering capacity to drive energy-related improvements, improving collaboration among these individuals will be critical.)

Mind-set, capabilities, and behaviors

In his master plan, John also defines initiatives needed to foster new mind-sets, capabilities, and behaviors.

John's initiatives

Initiatives in John's plan aimed at encouraging the right mind-set, capabilities, and behaviors include the following:

- Communicate the online survey results to the workforce to boost awareness of the importance of resource productivity and to get everyone think about how they can contribute to improving resource productivity in their own roles.

- Generate ideas for more effectively communicating about resource productivity within the site. For instance, one idea involves posting KPI results on hall posters to enable a "gallery walk"—whereby site managers and employees walk the hall, review the numbers, and discuss what they're seeing, whether it's progress or setbacks. These and other tactics will help build awareness as well as a sense of shared responsibility for improving resource productivity at the site.
- To address the lack of training he identified in the diagnose stage, establish a robust resource-productivity training program. Such a program could further raise awareness. Equally important, it could enable the site to develop a cadre of experts across functions who could help drive further change in the future.
- Develop workshops aimed at assessing managers' and employees' current beliefs regarding energy and yield productivity at the site and replacing them with more productive beliefs. At these workshops, attendees will learn about the skills they will need to support resource-productivity improvements in their roles and about the training programs that will be made available to them. When people agree that making specific changes is important and they believe they have the skills needed to make those changes, they are more likely to commit to the changes.

Having built a master plan showing initiatives needed to drive change in the site's technical system, management infrastructure, and mind-set, capabilities, and behaviors, John is ready to move on to the implement and sustain step.

Step 4: Implement and sustain

During the implement and sustain stage, John puts his master plan into action. He executes the technical system changes defined in the plan by ensuring that those responsible for each initiative know what they need to do, by when, and that they begin taking the required actions. He does the same with the changes he identified as critical for improving the site's management infrastructure as well as mind-set, capabilities, and behaviors.

At this point in the process, his role shifts from that of change agent to supporter. As supporter, he confirms that initiatives are on the right track, helps initiative leaders build tactical plans to roll out the projects they're responsible for, and aids them in addressing problems that arise.

Technical system

John focuses on realizing the potential savings and revenue gains (and thus margin improvements) identified for each initiative documented in his master plan. As the high-priority initiatives are rolled out, he and others at the site use the online RedE tool to measure the results and identify any problems, such as lower-than-expected savings, unanticipated delays, lack of needed resources such as personnel and funding, or higher than expected prices for new equipment needed for an initiative. Closely monitoring problems as they arise helps initiative leaders make needed midcourse corrections.

In addition, as the implementation of the high-priority initiatives moves from its first to its second year, site managers and initiative leaders begin identifying the next group of initiatives that will be given high priority. Of 500 projects identified in the master plan, 30 are implemented in the first year, and site leaders select another 60 to be implemented the following year.

Management infrastructure

Site leaders adopt the new KPIs and begin using results on those KPIs to conduct the new kinds of resource-productivity performance reviews and dialogues that John identified in the design and plan step. They also roll out the new capabilities in development training. John supports by coaching managers and supervisors in the performance dialogue over an extended period.

Mind-set, capabilities, and behaviors

John holds a kick-off event, at which he explains the background and goals of the resource-productivity-improvement program, the roles within the

A case in point: Sustaining change at a chemical player

Gains achieved through resource-productivity transformations can not only be sustained, they can also be magnified. For example, a chemical company based in North America had completed the implementation of an energy-efficiency program in 2010 that delivered a 15 percent reduction in energy costs within one and a half years. To achieve these improvements, the company performed an energy transformation focusing on its technical system, management infrastructure, and mind-set and behaviors with a strong focus on capability building at the site level to further ensure the sustainability of improvements.

In 2011, when the global financial crisis hit the company, it was better prepared, because the site had an additional cost advantage over the competition. But the company also used the new capabilities it had built to identify additional opportunities and to adapt to the new situation. All of this played a large role in its ability to manage the impact of the financial crisis.

program, the time line for the program, and the key findings from the diagnose step. He works with the line-management team to facilitate implementation of necessary changes and to instill root cause problem solving methods, such as "the five whys" technique and the fishbone diagram, into weekly joint production and engineering meetings.

In his role as supporter during the implement and sustain step, John and others at the site benefited from understanding several critical success factors related to effective site optimization.

Critical success factors during site optimization

Optimizing a site to deliver improvements in resource productivity is challenging not only from a technical perspective but also from a human one. Even if a company has mastered the prerequisites laid out in Chapter 8, skepticism may still run rampant, and resistance to change can come from stakeholders at every level and from any point of the organization. To overcome such hurdles, senior executives and change leaders must build and sustain momentum for change as well as bring the possibilities of resource productivity alive for people throughout the company. In the sections that follow, we explore approaches that can help.

Build on "mini T" momentum

For many manufacturers that launch a large-scale transformation effort to improve resource productivity, individual sites—along with the functions and departments within them—typically experience their own smaller-scale change efforts. For instance, one site successfully reduces energy consumption by upgrading a critical piece of equipment and by introducing a robust energy-performance dialogue after the site manager provides training for shop-floor employees to increase energy awareness and show them how to use the new configuration correctly.

We call such smaller changes "mini Ts" (for transformations) and maintain that they can serve as powerful forces for change across the rest of the organization. Specifically, a company that has successfully enhanced resource productivity for at least one production site—even in a minor way—can use lessons learned and share best practices from those experiences to achieve similar gains at a new site selected for optimization. "Mini Ts" thus constitute valuable training tools.

Savvy operations executives and change leaders will set up disciplined systems for capturing lessons and best practices from "mini Ts" and deploying them in sites that are just beginning their own change efforts.

Set up a rigorous performance-management system

A rigorous system for managing resource-productivity performance can serve as a kind of pacemaker for change at a production site that is being optimized. Essential components of such a performance-management system include defining resource-productivity KPIs, setting targets for each KPI, and establishing a regular schedule of performance-review meetings, during which leaders compare actual performance on KPIs against targets and make midcourse corrections as needed to close any gaps.

ISO 50001: Setting the stage for certification through resource-productivity improvement

Deftly executed, resource-productivity-improvement transformations almost automatically enable manufacturing sites to become certified as meeting ISO 50001 energy-management standards. ISO 50001 certification, in turn, delivers important benefits, including strengthening a company's reputation for environmental responsibility and opening doors to customers that want to buy from such companies and suppliers that want to sell to them. And because ISO 50001 certification may become a legal requirement in the future in the European Union, companies that achieve certification now will be way ahead of the game.

By rolling out a major resource-productivity program in 12 major industrial sites targeted for ISO 50001, an international chemical player head-quartered in Europe identified an opportunity to lower energy costs by 10 percent. It also enabled 3 of the 12 sites to achieve certification and laid the foundation for the remaining 9 sites to become ISO 50001 certified.

Successful resource-productivity programs position companies to meet the numerous key requirements of ISO 50001, which fall into five categories: governance and organization, plan, do, check, and act.

Setting up such a system sends a strong signal to everyone in the organization that executives and change leaders are taking the site-optimization program seriously. It also communicates expectations and enables people to recognize—and celebrate— successes, which is critical for maintaining momentum during any change effort.

A performance-management system is a central element in a company's management infrastructure, and executives can't afford to skimp on it. Simply put, no transformation journey can succeed without it.

ISO 50001 (Continued)

ISO 50001 requirements fall into five categories

Category	Requirements
Governance and organization	<ul><li>Appointment of top management representative for energy</li><li>Energy policy with clearly defined objectives and targets</li><li>Commitment to continuous improvement</li></ul>
Plan	<ul><li>Energy baseline established</li><li>Energy KPIs implemented</li><li>Energy objectives and targets defined</li></ul>
Do	<ul><li>Awareness created for energy-efficiency program</li><li>Ideas collected from employees and communicated</li><li>Standard operating procedures established</li></ul>
Check	<ul><li>Energy KPIs monitored, measured, and analyzed</li><li>Action plan effectiveness assessed</li><li>Internal audits conducted</li><li>Relevant documentation maintained</li></ul>
Act	<ul><li>Top management performance reviews conducted</li><li>Guidance provided by management for continuous improvement of the company's future energy policy</li></ul>

Activate four levers for exerting influence

In driving a site-optimization effort, executives and change leaders have at their disposal four powerful levers for exerting influence: insight and understanding, role modeling, skills, and aligned systems and structures. These levers can help them further motivate employees to adopt the everyday mind-set and behaviors needed to enhance resource productivity at the selected site.

- **Insight and understanding:** Leaders invite employees to jointly analyze current manufacturing processes to identify inefficiencies, losses, or resource waste and to assess energy consumption and costs at the site. Employees conclude, "I can see why we need to make this change."

- **Role modeling:** Leaders proactively address resource-productivity topics in all discussion forums, such as weekly meetings with teams or all-staff town-hall-style meetings. Leaders also develop train-the-trainer learning platforms to create change agents who can drive the transformation effort forward. Employees conclude, "If this change is so important to the higher-ups, it's probably important to me as well."

- **Skills:** Leaders set up committees in charge of executing on resource-productivity initiatives and specify members' responsibilities. They also create a targeted training module in the organization's learning platform. Employees conclude, "My company is going to help me build or acquire the competencies I need to make this change."

- **Aligned systems and structures:** Leaders develop a set of resource-productivity KPIs and targets, regularly track progress compared to targets, introduce energy audits, and specify new standard operating procedures. Employees conclude, "I know precisely what I need to do differently in my job and what goals we're all working towards."

When executives and change leaders activate these levers, they help employees make a step change away from indifference, resistance, and mindless compliance towards awareness, acceptance, and ability regarding the new tools and processes they need to use.

* * *

Optimizing a manufacturing site for maximum resource productivity requires mastery of a four-step process. Of course, excelling at the "harder" side of change, including identifying which technical system components need what modifications, is critical. But gains made in the technical system arena won't likely be sustained unless senior management and change leaders also excel at the "softer" side of change management. This includes understanding whence skepticism or resistance to new ways of doing work stems, exerting influence effectively, and helping employees acquire or strengthen the capabilities needed to do their work differently.

By attending to every variable in the change-management equation, manufacturers can achieve valuable improvements in a site's operations. Even more important, they can sustain those improvements as well as set the stage for capturing even greater gains in the future.

Chapter 10

YOUR NEXT STEPS

*C*ongratulations! In reading the preceding chapters in this book, you've absorbed extensive information about what resource productivity is, why it's so important, and how you can use unique, powerful tools and tactics to enhance it in your company's manufacturing operations. You've also seen what resource-productive operation (RPO) improvement tools and programs look like in action, through the numerous company case studies and examples provided in each chapter. If you're like many people we talk with, you're probably eager to get your company started on its RPO-improvement journey. But you're also likely wondering what steps you can take now to do so. That's what this chapter is all about.

Taking stock

We think that taking a few moments to step back and assess what you've learned so far can further stoke your enthusiasm for the subject and encourage you to explore a handful of specific actions you can initiate today to get started.

We've structured this chapter with those aims in mind. First we recap why companies—including yours—must act now to seize the RPO prize. We then sum up what resource productivity means for companies on every point of the supply circle and revisit all-too-common myths that are discouraging many executives, managers, and workers from embracing the concept of resource productivity. We quickly revisit the five core beliefs—and corresponding tools—needed to successfully implement a resource-productivity-improvement effort. In addition, we offer some advice on what you can do now, as well as whom to involve and how. And we close with another case study—this one about a renowned

US automotive OEM—to serve as a further source of inspiration and instruction.

Why act now?

As you saw in Chapter 1, a confluence of forces—including exploding population growth, rising per-capita wealth, and accelerating urbanization—is stepping up demand for resources. The increase in demand is happening even as other forces are making it more difficult and expensive to find and use new sources of supply. Demand for resources is thus outrunning supply.

The clash of these two sets of forces is creating a world where resource prices are already soaring and are expected to stay high. Meanwhile, owners of the most sought-after resources are making the biggest profits. Companies that buy from them are losing more and more control over their costs and seeing their margins shrink.

The situation is only going to get worse–unless companies act now. However, we don't at all think that the situation is just "gloom and doom." This "resource revolution" is also opening up new opportunities for manufacturers—in a broad range of sectors—that can learn how to maximize the productivity of the resources used in their operations. McKinsey analyses reveal large gaps between productivity gains that companies have already achieved and those they can accomplish by adopting the powerful new practices described in this book.

Indeed, we maintain that traditional tactics such as lean manufacturing won't be enough to solve the problem looming on the horizon. Instead, companies will need to master the discipline of getting more value (output, revenue, yield) from the resources they use in their manufacturing operations. We view resource productivity as "the next lean"—the follow-on wave in enhancing production operations.

To be sure, excelling at resource productivity will require new skills and a decidedly new mind-set. There's no time to waste, because the forces shaping this new landscape are only going to gain momentum. Still, what looks like a crisis will—if managed adroitly—constitute a critical opportunity. Our experience with clients has demonstrated that improving resource productivity is not only possible, it's also eminently doable.

Resource productivity: It's about more than just energy efficiency

Improving energy efficiency is an important element in enhancing resource productivity. But RPO is about much more than just energy efficiency. Such operations can produce critical gains for a company on multiple fronts:

- Energy—minimize energy use
- Raw materials—maximize raw-material conversion into finished product (yield)

- Emissions—minimize direct process emissions, such as CO_2, NO_x, and SO_x
- Water—reduce loss of water to the ecosystem and improve treatment and recovery from wastewater
- Waste—reduce or avoid waste streams and increase recycling or energy recovery
- Circularity—use new business models to capture value from supply circle

The tools and methods exist, and we've seen companies already reaping impressive benefits in the form of significant cost savings, higher revenue, and expanding profit margins. Yet resource-productivity exemplars will gain more than bottom-line improvements derived from double-digit cost savings paired with impressive improvements in resource yields. These companies will also have the satisfaction that comes from being better stewards of the planet's limited resources, benefiting the environment and society overall. Doing so also strengthens an enterprise's brand in the eyes of its stakeholders: from customers, suppliers, and employees to investors and partners.

Seizing the prize—no matter who you are

In Chapter 2, you saw that every company—no matter where it "sits" on its industry's supply circle—can enhance its resource productivity and achieve valuable gains while also strengthening the circle. That's true whether your company is an upstream manufacturer, a downstream manufacturer, or a collection and sorting (waste management) business.

Moreover, regardless of your enterprise's position on the supply circle, you and others in the organization don't have to be constrained by long-held, widespread myths about resource productivity. Instead, you can challenge such myths and replace them with the following realities:

- Even when energy is cheap, it's still a large cost.
- Resource-productivity investments can have a good payback period.
- Energy is core to your company's operations.
- Energy impact can be measured and managed.
- Resource yield in your enterprise can be further improved.

Revisiting the five core beliefs

In Chapters 3 through 7, you explored the five core beliefs in detail—radical new ways of thinking—that form the foundation of our RPO framework. And you learned about specific tools and methodologies that can help you turn each belief into effective action.

For example, you discovered how to do the following:

- "Think lean" by leveraging lean principles and using lean expertise already available in your organization to build an RPO strategy.
- "Think limits" by using the theoretical-limit concept to set ambitious goals that foster creative thinking and deliver significant resource-productivity improvements.
- "Think profit per hour" by reviewing the full profit equation (all revenue and cost components) when making changes aimed at improving resource productivity.
- "Think holistic" by making necessary modifications to your management infrastructure as well as to mind-sets, capabilities, and behaviors throughout your organization to reinforce changes made to your technical system.

- "Think circular" by viewing your product as your future resources and collaborating to optimize the overall supply circle.

Armed with a solid understanding of these five core beliefs, your next steps towards fostering resource productivity in your organization stand the best possible chance of succeeding.

Laying the groundwork

In Chapter 8, you found suggestions for laying the groundwork for a successful resource-productivity-improvement program in your organization. These included mastering prerequisites such as aligning top management, establishing the right management infrastructure, developing a sound communication plan, and crafting a plan for building or strengthening the capabilities and expertise you'll need to drive successful change.

In Chapter 9, you discovered how an effort focused on enhancing resource productivity at a manufacturing site works in practice. You read about the four steps that the program travels through: prepare, diagnose, design and plan, and implement and sustain. And you saw which activities and tools during each phase were most closely associated with the three major dimensions of an RPO-transformation program: operating system, management infrastructure, and mind-set, capabilities, and behavior.

Taking your next steps

Now we come to the crux of this chapter: what you, personally, can and should do now to get your organization moving down the path to more productive management of your resources. We think that the following tips are a great place to start.

Learn even more

You've read this book. You've learned about our unique approach and tools. You've seen how companies are using the RPO framework to generate impressive results. Now learn even more about it. For instance, take a tour of a model factory and ask people who have experienced this training forum what new insights and best practices they've gleaned. Attend conferences on the subject of resource productivity, energy efficiency, and other related topics. Conduct "lunch and learns," at which attendees read a chapter from this book and then discuss how to put the ideas to use. Visit other companies—in your industry as well as in other industries—that have made progress in this area. If you haven't already done so, sign up for access to McKinsey's

Spotlight on how to exert influence

Who should initiate an RPO effort in a manufacturing organization? Anyone can do so—from C-suite executives such as the CEO and chief operating officer (COO) to energy managers, plant managers, and line leaders. But regardless of where you are in your company's reporting hierarchy, you'll need to master the art of exerting influence in order to win support for your proposed initiative. That's because you'll almost certainly have to persuade others over whom you don't have formal authority to approve funding for the program or help execute the changes needed to make the program a success. Of course, if you're a member of the executive committee, you'll have an easier time persuading others in the organization to get on board. In fact, the most successful RPO change programs typically have strong backing from top management. But if you're a few levels below the C-suite—such as the energy manager at a production site in a company that has hundreds of such sites—you'll need to influence your direct superiors and possibly their peers to support the change program you're proposing. You may even have to persuade your own peers to back you, and certainly your direct reports will play an important role in executing the changes you want. What's the best way to win higher-ups' support for an RPO initiative in your group? Identify one or two manageable free Operations Extranet—*http://operations-extranet.mckinsey.com*—and join the 30,000 subscribers already benefiting from this information source.

Spread the word

Discuss the concepts and practices in this book with peers, employees, and supervisors in your organization. Relate the most impressive statistics

"quick wins" (versus trying to "boil the whole ocean") that you can achieve by applying RPO tools and methodologies described in this book. Pick projects that will deliver quantifiable results. Score those successes—then communicate them to decision makers in your organization. In effect, you'll be saying something like, "I used these tools, they worked, and I was able to cut our energy usage by 10 percent. I suggest rolling out the same program to other sites."

But don't stop there. Offer your assistance in implementing RPO changes at other sites. For instance, explain that you'll share best practices and lessons learned from your site's experiences with change agents and leaders at other sites. And be sure to involve decision makers and opinion leaders from those other sites in designing RPO change projects. You'll likely gain helpful input and ideas from them. Contributing ideas also tends to make people feel a sense of ownership over the project in question. And when people feel that they "own" the project (or at least a piece of it), they're more likely to commit to it as well as stick with the effort during the inevitable setbacks. Finally, they're more likely to spread the word about the effort. Thus, by getting others' input on how to drive positive change, you can transform even the toughest skeptic into a powerful multiplier.

you found in these pages. Talk about how your company might try applying a particular concept or practice to test the RPO waters and to begin planting seeds of change.

Get a granular picture

If you're a plant manager, you probably have one energy bill for your entire plant. That's not granular enough to assess resource productivity in your current operations. You need to break down the total bill into different departments, processes, equipment, and so forth. So start collecting historical data on your group's costs—over the course of two or three months, to get the most meaningful data and start quickly. Look at the patterns, and come up with answers to the following questions: What resources have we been spending the most money on? Where does each resource tend to go; that is, which departments or functions within the organization? Which processes? Which pieces of equipment? Which products or services? Building this granular picture is the best way to pinpoint the most promising opportunities to enhance resource productivity in your plant's operations.

Try it out

Whether you manage a team, function, department, or entire site, identify specific tools and practices you could deploy in your group now to begin scoring some "quick wins" in the area of resource-productivity improvement. For instance, something as seemingly minor as including resource productivity as a regular agenda item for strategy and operations planning meetings could boost awareness of the topic and lead to new continuous-improvement initiatives. If your effort doesn't deliver the hoped-for results, analyze what went well and what didn't, and why, then use what you've learned to launch a better initiative. And don't be afraid to ask for help from people in other parts of the organization. For example, if you're an energy manager at a site, connect with your peers at other sites to explore the challenges, opportunities, and best practices for RPO.

A case in point: Achieving the next "green" horizon at Ford Motor Company

Michigan, US-based Ford Motor Company has a long track record of success. Founded in 1903, the company today sells a wide range of vehicles as well as auto parts around the globe. In 2013 alone, it recorded revenues of USD 147 billion. It employs 181,000 people and has operations on nearly every continent.

In the early 2000s, Ford realized that while it made progress on the resource-productivity front, it was still falling behind competitors in such areas as energy use, water consumption, and waste production. The company set a number of ambitious goals—including reducing CO_2 emissions in its US facilities by 10 percent per vehicle by 2012, as part of an Alliance of Automobile Manufacturers program; reducing water use per vehicle by 3 percent per year; improving energy efficiency by 3 percent per year going forward; and reducing landfill disposal by 10 percent each year, including through the use of recycled, renewable, and lightweight materials. Ford then launched initiatives aimed at achieving these goals. For example:

- **Facilities emissions.** Adopt a new paint process that eliminates the need for paint to cure after the prime coat. Power down all desktop and notebook computers at night.
- **Water usage.** Use minimum quantity lubricant machining, to lubricate cutting tools with a small amount of oil sprayed.
- **Energy consumption.** Improve operational efficiency of large compressors by implementing a network-controlled system.
- **Waste reduction.** Convert the entire fleet to use bio-based foam seating. Use post-consumer recycled resins (detergent bottles, tires, battery casings) to make underbody systems.

As a key part of Ford's RPO transformation program, senior managers made a half-day visit to an advanced "green" model factory in Munich in 2011. The factory, a partnership between McKinsey and the Technical University of Munich, replicates a real production environment and produces recognizable products.

In addition to demonstrating lean concepts, it includes learning modules centered on energy, water, waste and by-products, and emissions.

Ford then selected a group of 50 employees—engineers and mid-level and plant managers—to participate in a week-long training program at the factory, in two groups of 25. The training program concentrated on helping attendees see energy from a new perspective, learn how to use energy efficient tools, and begin deploying those tools to support the achievement of Ford's RPO goals. Key modules in the training included:

- Identifying energy losses
- Learning about diagnostic methods and tools
- Prioritizing technical system improvement opportunities
- Measuring resource-productivity performance
- Becoming a change agent
- Learning from case examples
- Making mind-set and behavior changes.

As a result of these experiences, Ford decided to integrate energy management into its global manufacturing system—adding it to existing priorities such as environmental responsibility, safety, and productivity. The model factory experience also enabled Ford to build on earlier RPO efforts it had made—compounding its success in this area.

The company's achievements speak for themselves:

- **Facility-related emissions.** Since 2000, Ford's North American operations have cut volatile organic compounds (VOC) emissions associated with the painting process (by far its largest source of VOC emissions) by 50 percent. In 2013, these operations emitted 16.8 grams of VOCs per square meter of surface coated, down from 18 grams in 2011. Because the control equipment used to reduce VOC emissions consumes significant amounts of energy, Ford has worked to identify innovative approaches to painting that meet cost, quality, and production goals while allowing the company to reduce energy use significantly and maintain environmental compliance. For example, Ford developed a Paint Emissions Concentrator (PEC) technology (formerly referred to as "fumes-to-fuel"), which uses a fluidized bed adsorber and desorber and condensation equipment to collect and concentrate solvent emissions into liquid form. The intent of the technology is to collect a portion of the VOCs from the spray-booth exhaust, super-concentrate them in the paint emissions concentrator, then condense and store them on site for use as a fuel source. In this way, the solvent emissions are recycled back into the production process and overall VOC emissions are reduced. Ford is currently working with a Canadian university to drive development of the PEC technology and evaluate the potential for producing and using hydrogen fuel.

- **Water consumption.** Water conservation is an integral part of Ford's sustainability strategy.

Many vehicle-manufacturing processes require water, and water is used at every point in the company's supply chain. Ford's water-related risks come not only from being a direct water consumer, but from being a large purchaser of water-intensive materials, parts, and components. Ford set a global manufacturing water-use-per-vehicle reduction goal of 30 percent by 2015, using a 2009 baseline, and achieved this goal in 2013, two years ahead of schedule. Ford is upading its global manufacturing water strategy in 2014 and setting a new long-term target. Ford is a signatory to the UN CEO Water Mandate and became one of the first companies to join the CDP's Water Disclosure program to promote conservation and stewardship.

- **Energy use and efficiency.** In 2012, Ford established a five-year objective to improve its operational energy use per vehicle globally by 25 percent by the end of 2016, based on a 2011 baseline normalized for weather and production. In 2013, it improved global energy efficiency by 17.4 percent against a 2011 year baseline normalized for weather and production levels. The company reduced its overall facilities-related CO_2 emissions by 51 percent, or 5 million metric tons, from 2000 to 2013. During this same period, it reduced facilities-related CO_2 emissions per vehicle by 46 percent. Its total CO_2 emissions increased from 2012 to 2013 by 0.6 percent, while CO_2 emissions per vehicle decreased by 9 percent during that period. (Total CO_2 emissions from facilities increased slightly from 2012 to 2013 due to increases in production. However, CO_2 emissions per vehicle decreased, reflecting greater efficiency.) The company has met its commitment to reduce US facility emissions by 10 percent per vehicle produced between 2002 and 2012, as part of an Alliance of Automobile Manufacturers program. It became the first automaker to join The Climate Registry, a voluntary carbon disclosure project that links several state-sponsored efforts focused on greenhouse gas emissions reporting.

- **Waste.** In 2013, Ford introduced a new plan to reduce waste sent to landfills by 40 percent on a per vehicle basis between 2011 and 2016 globally. Ford has already reduced global per vehicle waste sent to landfills by 40 percent from 2007 to 2011. In 2013, Ford facilities globally sent approximately 49,800 metric tons of waste to landfills, a reduction of 5.4 percent from 2012.

These successes enabled Ford to capture such impressive savings that the global head of operations shared Ford's RPO story with other companies working with McKinsey to implement new RPO programs. His actions further demonstrated the value and inspiration that can be created when companies exchange insights, best practices, and lessons learned with one another.

ABOUT THE AUTHORS

Markus Hammer
Senior Knowledge Expert, Vienna, Austria

As a seasoned, internationally experienced operations consultant, Markus utilizes a deep knowledge of lean and green operations and a  passion for capability building to help clients. He has delivered significant impact in large-scale operations-transformation programs and proven both his functional and project leadership skills.

He is a core member of the faculty in McKinsey's global Capability Center network and has a strong track record of designing and delivering distinctive trainings. Recent initiatives include establishing the "Executive Operations Experience," a joint program with the Kellogg School of Management, and serving as lecturer at Graz University of Technology.

Prior to McKinsey, Markus worked as the site integrated working system leader (productivity improvements, TPM, and organizational excellence) and a process and project engineer at Procter & Gamble. Markus holds a master of science degree in process engineering and environmental technologies and studied at Graz University of Technology and the University of Strathclyde in Glasgow. He conducted research on "Corporate Sustainability Performance Evaluation" at the Instituto Nacional de Engenharia, Tecnologia e Inovação in Lisbon.

Ken Somers
Master Expert, Antwerp, Belgium

Ken is one of the firm's master experts on resource-productive operations (energy, yield, environmental cost, and throughput) and leader of the McKinsey Manufacturing Practice (MMP) Resource Productive Operations service line. He has done extensive operational work in the manufacturing industry and has been dedicated to the topic of resource productivity for the last six years. In addition, he has led multiple engagements on operational and design improvement for energy and yield in steel, metals, pulp and paper, refining, chemicals, pharmaceuticals, packaged goods, and retail.

His client work spans a wide field covering quick diagnostics, resource-productive-operation transformations, training of resource-productivity expert groups, coaching of client experts, and development of IT-enabled improvement through RedE. He is one of the key faculty members of McKinsey's energy-efficiency model factory network.

Prior to McKinsey, Ken worked on the promotion of science-technology research in industry (IWT) in the chemistry lab of Arnout Ceulemans at the Katholieke Universiteit (KU) Leuven and obtained a PhD in theoretical chemistry (focus: protein modeling and spectroscopy).

He also holds a chemistry degree with "Great Distinction" from the KU Leuven, and an academic degree in teaching.

For more information please contact
Markus_Hammer@mckinsey.com or
Ken_Somers@mckinsey.com

WEB-BASED RESOURCES

Resource-productive operation is the next level of lean, using classic lean and resource-productivity-focused approaches to expand into full variable margin optimization (energy cost reductions of 10 to 15 percent, yield improvements of 2 to 5 percent), applying new concepts such as profit per hour, theoretical resource-productivity limits, value in use, advanced analytics, and IT-based supplier development over the full production cycle. We hope this book has inspired you to embark on the journey required to achieve meaningful resource productivity improvement. The web-based tools and approaches below may be another helpful step on that journey for some readers.

- RedE, a Web-based solution for energy efficiency across suppliers: *http://apps.mckinsey. com/RedE*
- Benchmarking your organization's Energy Productivity (requires free sign up to McKinsey's Operations Extranet: *https://operations-extranet.mckinsey.com/content/ Benchmarking+tools/view/2014_energy_productivity_bench-marking_tool*
- Information about a network of green model factories to build resource productivity operational capabilities (Atlanta, Beijing, Singapore, Munich, Lyon, Luxembourg): *http://www.capability-center.mckinsey.com*

REFERENCES

Achieving economic and environmental win-wins with resource-productive operations
Hella Schmidt, Jelmer Ikink, and Markus Hammer *http://operations-extranet.mckinsey.com/*, accessed June 30, 2014.

A COO's energy efficiency primer: Responses to five common myths
Markus Hammer and Ken Somers
http://operations-extranet.mckinsey.com/, accessed June 30, 2014.

Advanced analytics and resource-productive manufacturing
Ritesh Awasthi, Thomas Koch Blank, Markus Hammer, and Ken Somers
http://operations-extranet.mckinsey.com/, accessed June 30, 2014.

Are you ready for the resource revolution?
Stefan Heck and Matt Rogers, McKinsey Quarterly
http://www.mckinsey.com/insights/sustainability/are_you_ready_for_the_resource_revolution/, accessed July 28, 2014.

Bringing energy efficiency to the fab
Steve Chen, Apoorv Gautam, and Florian Weig
McKinsey on Semiconductors, Number 3, autumn 2013 *http://www.mckinsey.com/client_service/semiconductors/latest_thinking/autumn_2013_issue*, accessed June 30, 2014.

REFERENCES

Capability for Performance—The Path to Excellence: Chapter 3: Model factories create conviction and confidence
Tomas Koch, Stephen Bear, et al., McKinsey, May 2012.

Defining a multisite operational strategy
Wim Gysegom and Ken Somers
http://operations-extranet.mckinsey.com/, accessed June 30, 2014.

Demystify your energy use
Thomas Koch Blank
http://operations-extranet.mckinsey.com/, accessed June 30, 2014.

Finding Opportunity in Uncertainty: A New Paradigm for Pharmaceutical Supply Chains, McKinsey, 2014.

Five core beliefs on resource-productive operations—an infographic
Markus Hammer and Ken Somers
http://operations-extranet.mckinsey.com/, accessed June 30, 2014.

From supply chains to supply circles
http://www.mckinsey.com/features/circular_economy, accessed June 30, 2014.

Future-proofing: Taking the long view on sustainable product development (Parts 1 & 2)
Eric Hannon and Stephan Mohr
http://operations-extranet.mckinsey.com/, accessed June 30, 2014.

How big data can improve manufacturing
Eric Auschitzky, Markus Hammer, and Agesan Rajagopaul
http://www.mckinsey.com/Insights/Operations/How_big_data_can_improve_manufacturing?cid=DigitalEdge-eml-alt-mip-mck-oth-1407, accessed July 3, 2014.

How advanced analytics will power the next wave of process optimization in manufacturing
Eric Auschitzky, Markus Hammer, Agesan Rajagopaul, and Ken Somers
http://operations-extranet.mckinsey.com/, accessed June 30, 2014.

Making green manufacturing pay
Kirill Koutchai, Lars Markworth, Tom Niemann, and Ken Somers
http://operations-extranet.mckinsey.com/, accessed June 30, 2014.

Manufacturing resource productivity
Stephan Mohr, Ken Somers, Steven Swartz, and Helga Vanthournout
McKinsey on Sustainability & Resource Productivity
http://www.mckinsey.com/insights/sustainability/manufacturing_resource_productivity, accessed July 28, 2014.

McKinsey on resource-productive operations—opportunity for a new generation
Jochen Latz
http://operations-extranet.mckinsey.com, accessed June 30, 2014.

Measuring the real cost of water
Kimberly Henderson, Ken Somers, and Martin Stuchtey, McKinsey Quarterly
http://www.mckinsey.com/insights/sustainability/measuring_the_real_cost_of_water, accessed July 28, 2014.

Profiting from compliance [ISO50001]
Markus Hammer, Peter Odenwalder, and Ken Somers
http://operations-extranet.mckinsey.com/, accessed June 30, 2014.

Remaking the industrial economy
Hanh Nguyen, Martin Stuchtey, and Markus Zils, McKinsey Quarterly
http://www.mckinsey.com/insights/manufacturing/remaking_the_industrial_economy, accessed July 28, 2014.

REFERENCES

Resource-productive manufacturing: Use fewer resources, make more money
Raffaele Carpi, Markus Hammer, Marcus Jacob, and Ken Somers
http://operations-extranet.mckinsey.com/, accessed June 30, 2014.

Resource-productive operations: Closing the capability gap
Harsh Choudhry, Markus Hammer, and Ken Somers
http://operations-extranet.mckinsey.com/, accessed June 30, 2014.

Resource revolution: Meeting the world's energy, materials, food, and water needs
McKinsey Global Institute, McKinsey Sustainability and Resource-Productivity Practice
http://www.mckinsey.com/insights/energy_resources_materials/resource_revolution, accessed July 28, 2014.

Resource revolution: How to capture the biggest business opportunity in a century
Stefan Heck, Matt Rogers, and Paul Carroll
http://www.mckinsey.com/client_service/sustainability/latest_thinking/resource_ revolution_book, accessed July 28, 2014.

Seizing China's energy efficiency opportunity: A case study, Steve Chen
Maxine Fu and Arthur Wang, McKinsey Quarterly
http://www.mckinsey.com/insights/energy_resources_materials/seizing_chinas_energy-efficiency_opportunity, accessed July 28, 2014.

Towards the Circular Economy: Economic and business rationale for an accelerated transition
Volume 1, Ellen MacArthur Foundation
http://www.ellenmacarthurfoundation.org/business/reports/ce2012, accessed July 28, 2014.

Towards the Circular Economy: Opportunities for the consumer goods sector
Volume 2, Ellen MacArthur Foundation
http://www.ellenmacarthurfoundation.org/business/reports/ce2013,
accessed July 28, 2014.

Towards the Circular Economy: Accelerating the scale-up across global supply chains
Volume 3, Ellen MacArthur Foundation
http://www.ellenmacarthurfoundation.org/business/reports/ce2014,
accessed July 28, 2014.

ACKNOWLEDGMENTS

First and foremost, we would like to show our gratitude to all our clients and colleagues with whom we have had the opportunity to work over the last decade at McKinsey. They provided rich examples and analyses on which we could build to create this book.

We would like to thank our editors, Mary Brandt Kerr, Catherine Cuddihee, Jeff Garigliano, Lauren Keller Johnson, John Kerr, and Edward Ruehle; our design team, Barbara Bachhuber (layout and illustrations) and Bettina Hauber (business graphics); and our proofreading team, Donna Felten and Kristina Leppien.

We also benefited from the support of Nick Bennette, Harsh Choudhry, Pol-Axel Colart, Stephen Doig, Maxine Fu, Stefan Knupfer, Amy Radermacher, Malgorzata Sliczna, Joris Van Niel, Helga Vanthournout, and the global "Resource-Productive Operations" community.

A special thanks to John Fleming and Alain Michel for sharing their company success stories.

And finally, we would like to thank our families for their patience, encouragement, and love!

We have thanked a lot of people who have all played a role in completing this book. Any errors or omissions remain our own responsibility.

43363385R00136

Made in the USA
Middletown, DE
07 May 2017